Financial Reporting & Analysis:
Using Financial Accounting Information

8th Edition

Charles H. Gibson

The University of Toledo

SOUTH-WESTERN
✳
THOMSON LEARNING

Australia · Canada · Mexico · Singapore · Spain · United Kingdom · United States

Financial Reporting Analysis: Using Financial Accounting Information Test Bank
   by Gibson

Acquisitions Editor: Rochelle Kronzek
Developmental Editor: Ken Martin
Marketing Manager: Larry Qualls
Production Editor: Marci Dechter
Manufacturing Coordinator: Doug Wilke
Cover Design: Modern Design
Cover Illustration: copyright 1999 PhotoDisc
Printer: Globus

Printed in the United States of America
1 2 3 4 5 03 02 01 00

For more information contact South-Western College Publishing, 5101 Madison Road,
Cincinnati, Ohio, 45227 or find us on the Internet at http://www.swcollege.com

For permission to use material from this text or product, contact us by
• **telephone: 1-800-730-2214**
• **fax: 1-800-730-2215**
• **web: http://www.thomsonrights.com**

0-324-02359-6

This book is printed on acid-free paper.

TABLE OF CONTENTS

Chapter 1: INTRODUCTION TO FINANCIAL REPORTING

MULTIPLE CHOICE

d 1. Charging off equipment that cost less than $20 would be
an example of the application of:
   a. going concern
   b. cost
   c. matching
   d. materiality
   e. realization

c 2. The going concern assumption:
   a. is applicable to all financial statements
   b. primarily involves periodic income measurement
   c. must be adhered to in order for the statements to be
      prepared under generally accepted accounting
      principles
   d. requires that accounting procedures be the same from
      period to period
   e. none of the above

e 3. Understating assets and revenues is justified based on:
   a. realization assumption
   b. matching
   c. materiality
   d. realization
   e. none of the above

a 4. The assumption that enables us to prepare periodic
statements between the time that a business commences
operations and the time it goes out of business is:
   a. time period
   b. business entity
   c. historical cost
   d. transaction
   e. none of the above

c 5. Valuing assets at their liquidation values is **not**
consistent with:
   a. conservatism
   b. materiality
   c. going concern
   d. time period
   e. none of the above

c   6. The business being separate and distinct from the owners
        is an integral part of the:
        a. time period assumption
        b. going concern assumption
        c. business entity assumption
        d. realization assumption
        e. none of the above

e   7. This principle assumes that the reader of the financial
        statements is interested in the liquidation values:
        a. conservatism
        b. matching
        c. time period
        d. realization
        e. none of the above

c   8. An accounting period that ends when operations are at a
        low ebb is:
        a. a calendar year
        b. a fiscal year
        c. the natural business year
        d. an operating year
        e. none of the above

a   9. The accounting principle that assumes that inflation
        will **not** take place or will be immaterial is:
        a. monetary unit
        b. historical cost
        c. realization
        d. going concern
        e. none of the above

d   10. Valuing inventory at the lower of cost or market is an
        application of the:
        a. time period assumption
        b. realization principle
        c. going concern principle
        d. conservatism principle
        e. none of the above

d   11. The realization principle leads accountants to normally
        recognize revenue at:
        a. the end of production
        b. during production
        c. the receipt of cash
        d. the point of sale
        e. none of the above

d   12.   The comment that it is proper for items that are not
          material to be handled in the most expedient and
          economical manner possible on the financial statements
          is representative of:
          a. matching
          b. conservatism
          c. realization
          d. materiality
          e. none of the above

a   13.   This assumption deals with when to recognize the costs
          that are associated with the revenue that is being
          recognized:
          a. matching
          b. going concern
          c. consistency
          d. materiality
          e. none of the above

e   14.   The most significant current source of generally
          accepted accounting principles:
          a. New York Stock Exchange
          b. Accounting Principles Board
          c. Accounting Research Studies
          d. AICPA committee on Accounting Procedure
          e. Financial Accounting Standards Board

d   15.   All but one of these responses indicates a difference
          between the Financial Accounting Standards Board (FASB)
          and prior approaches. Select the one that is **not** a
          difference.
          a. The FASB is independent of the AICPA.
          b. The size of the board is much smaller.
          c. The FASB has broader representation.
          d. The FASB is the primary board for the development of
              generally accepted accounting principles.
          e. Members of the FASB serve on a full-time basis.

a   16.   The Accounting Principles Board issued Opinions between:
          a. 1960-1973
          b. 1939-1959
          c. 1973-present
          d. 1966-1976
          e. none of the above

b   17.   Accountants face a problem of when to recognize revenue. Which of the following methods of recognizing revenue is **not** used in practice?
a. point of sale
b. point of order acceptance
c. end of production
d. receipt of cash
e. revenue recognized during production

c   18.   The following data relate to Swift Company for the year ended December 31, 2000. Swift Company uses the accrual basis.

Sales on credit	$250,000
Cost of inventory sold on credit	170,000
Collections from customers	220,000
Purchase of inventory on credit	150,000
Payment for purchases	140,000
Selling expenses (accrual basis)	40,000
Payment for selling expenses	45,000

Which of the following amounts represents income for Swift Company for the year ended December 31, 2000?
a. $60,000
b. $50,000
c. $40,000
d. $35,000
e. $30,000

b   19.   The following data relate to Rocket Company for the year ended December 31, 2000. Rocket Company uses the cash basis.

Sales on credit	$180,000
Cost of inventory sold on credit	130,000
Collections from customers	170,000
Purchase of inventory on credit	140,000
Payment for purchases	150,000
Selling expenses (accrual basis)	20,000
Payment for selling expenses	25,000

Which of the following amounts represents income for Rocket Company for the year ended December 31, 2000?
a. $30,000
b. $ 5,000 loss
c. $40,000
d. $45,000
e. $50,000

TRUE/FALSE

T   1.   In order to determine the economic success of a grocery
           store we should view it as separate from the other
           resources that are owned by this individual.

T   2.   Many of our present financial statement figures would be
           misleading if it were not for the going concern
           assumption.

F   3.   The going concern assumption does **not** influence the
           classification of assets and liabilities.

T   4.   The only accurate way to account for the success or
           failure of an entity is to accumulate all transactions
           from the opening of business until the business
           eventually liquidates.

T   5.   Usually not until the inventory is sold in the normal
           course of business can the entity reasonably account for
           the profits related to the inventory.

T   6.   To the extent that money does not remain stable, it
           loses its usefulness as the standard for measuring
           financial transactions.

T   7.   A loss in value of money is called inflation.

T   8.   At the time of originally recording a transaction,
           historical cost also represents the fair market value.

F   9.   It would be conservative to value inventory at market.

F   10.   Accountants normally recognize revenue when cash is
           received.

T   11.   The 1933 and 1934 United States federal securities laws
           virtually gave the Securities and Exchange Commission
           (SEC) authority and responsibility for the development
           of generally accepted accounting principles.

T   12.   The Statements of Financial Accounting Concepts are
           intended to provide the Financial Accounting Standards
           Board with a common foundation and the basic underlying
           reasoning on which to consider the merits of various
           alternative accounting principles.

T   13.   Eventually, the Financial Accounting Standards Board
           intends to evaluate current principles in terms of the
           concepts established in the Financial Accounting
           Concepts.

F   14. Financial Accounting Concepts establish generally accepted accounting principles.

T   15. According to the second Financial Accounting Concept, those characteristics of information that make it a desirable commodity can be viewed as a hierarchy of qualities, with understandability and usefulness for decision making of most importance.

T   16. Performance indicators for non-business organizations are usually formal budgets and donor restrictions.

T   17. Reasonable inaccuracies of accounting for an entity, short of its complete life span, are accepted.

T   18. Using the business entity assumption, the financial statements are prepared separate and distinct from the owners of the entity.

F   19. The time period assumption indicates that the entity will remain in business for an indefinite period time.

F   20. Timeliness is a pervasive constraint imposed upon financial accounting information.

T   21. Relevance and reliability are two primary qualities that make accounting information useful for decision making.

F   22. Predictive value, feedback value, and timeliness are ingredients needed to ensure that the information is reliable.

F   23. Decision usefulness is a pervasive constraint imposed upon financial accounting information.

T   24. Relevance is a quality requiring that the information be timely and that it also have predictive value or feedback value or both.

T   25. The SEC has the authority to determine generally accepted accounting principles and to regulate the accounting profession.

T   26. Some industry practices lead to accounting reports that do not conform to the general theory that underlies accounting.

F   27. All important events that influence the prospects for the entity are recorded and, therefore, are reflected in the financial statements.

T   28.   The accrual basis of accounting recognizes revenue when
          realized (realization concept) and expenses when
          incurred (matching concept).

T   29.   The cash basis recognizes revenue when cash is received
          and recognizes expenses when cash is paid.

T   30.   The accountant records only events that affect the
          financial position of the entity and, at the same time,
          can be reasonably determined in monetary terms.

PROBLEMS

1.

Required:
Listed below are several accounting principles and assumptions.
Match the letter of each with the appropriate statement.

a.   Business entity   e.   Historical cost   i.   Full disclosure
b.   Going concern   f.   Conservatism   j.   Verifiability
c.   Time period   g.   Realization   k.   Materiality
d.   Monetary unit   h.   Consistency   l.   Industry practices

   1.   Some industry practices lead to accounting reports that do
        not conform to the general theory that underlies
        accounting.

   2.   Requires the accountant to adhere as closely as possible to
        verifiable data.

   3.   Requires the entity to give the same treatment to
        comparable transactions.

   4.   Directs that the measurement that has the least favorable
        effect on net income and financial position in the current
        period be selected.

   5.   The decision is made to accept some inaccuracy because of
        incomplete information about the future in exchange for
        more timely reporting.

   6.   Involves the relative size and importance of an item to a
        firm.

   7.   A reasonable summarization of financial information is
        required.

   8.   Deals with the problem of when to recognize revenue.

   9.   The primary value that is used for financial statements.

10. Standard of measure for financial statements.

11. The assumption that the entity being accounted for will remain in business for an indefinite period of time.

12. Assumption that a business's financial statements are separate and distinct from the personal transactions of the owners.

SOLUTION:

1.	l	4.	f	7.	i	10.	d
2.	j	5.	c	8.	g	11.	b
3.	h	6.	k	9.	e	12.	a

2.

Required:
State the accounting principle or assumption that is most applicable:

a. The company uses the same accounting principle from period to period.

b. Financial statements are prepared periodically.

c. Subscriptions paid in advance are recorded as unearned subscription income.

d. All significant financial transactions are reported.

e. Personal transactions of the stockholders are not recorded on the company's financial statements.

f. Land is recorded at $10,000, which was the amount paid. Current value of the land is $25,000.

g. The accountants determine that the company is in danger of going bankrupt and, therefore, refuse to certify the statements as prepared according to generally accepted accounting principles.

h. The company loses a major customer and does not record a loss.

SOLUTION:

a.	consistency	e.	business entity
b.	time period	f.	historical cost
c.	realization	g.	going concern
d.	full disclosure	h.	transaction approach

3.

Listed below are ten interrelated elements that are directly related to measuring performance and status of an enterprise according to SFAC No. 6, "Elements of Financial Statements."

a. Assets
b. Liabilities
c. Equity
d. Investments by owners
e. Distribution to owners
f. Comprehensive income
g. Revenues
h. Expenses
i. Gains
j. Losses

Required:
Match the letter with the appropriate definition.

1. Probable future sacrifices of economic benefits arising from present obligations of a particular entity to transfer assets or provide services to other entities in the future as a result of past transactions or events.

2. Increases in the equity of a particular business enterprise resulting from transfers to the enterprise from other entities of something of value to obtain or increase ownership interests (or equity) in it. Assets are most commonly received as investments by owners, but that which is received may also include services or satisfaction or conversion of liabilities of the enterprise.

3. A decrease in the equity of a particular business enterprise resulting from transferring assets, rendering services, or incurring liabilities by the enterprise to owners. Decreases ownership interest (or equity) in an enterprise.

4. Decreases in the equity (net assets) from peripheral or incidental transactions of an entity and from all other transactions and other events and circumstances affecting the entity during a period, except those that result from expenses or distributions to owners.

5. Outflows or other consumption or using up of assets or incurrences of liabilities (or a combination of both) from delivering or producing goods, rendering services, or carrying out other activities that constitute the entity's ongoing major or central operations.

6. The change in equity (net assets) of a business enterprise during a period from transactions and other events and circumstances from nonowner sources. It includes all changes in equity during a period, except those resulting from investments by owners and distributions to owners.

7. Probable future economic benefits obtained or controlled by a particular entity as a result of past transactions or events.

8. The residual interest in the assets of an entity after deducting its liabilities.

9. Inflows or other enhancements of assets of an entity or settlements of its liabilities (or a combination of both) from delivering or producing goods, rendering services, or engaging in other activities that constitute the entity's ongoing major or central operations.

10. Increases in the equity (net assets) from peripheral or incidental transactions of an entity and from all other transactions and other events and circumstances from revenues or investments by owners.

SOLUTION:

1.	b		6.	f
2.	d		7.	a
3.	e		8.	c
4.	j		9.	g
5.	h		10.	i

4. Listed below are ten phrases with the appropriate acronym.

   a. Generally accepted accounting principles (GAAP)
   b. Securities and exchange commission (SEC)
   c. American institute of certified public accountants (AICPA)
   d. Accounting principles board (APB)
   e. Financial accounting standards board (FASB)
   f. Statements of financial standards (SFAS)
   g. Discussion memorandum (DM)
   h. Statements of position (SOP)
   i. Emerging issues task force (EITF)
   j. Financial reporting releases (FRRs)

Required:
Match the letter with the appropriate definition.

1. Issued by the SEC and give the SEC's official position on matters relating to financial reports.

2. Accounting principles that have substantial authoritative support.

3. A task force of representatives from the accounting profession created by the FASB to deal with emerging issues of financial reporting.

4. Created by the Securities Exchange Act of 1934.

5. Issued by the Accounting Standards Division of the AICPA to influence the development of accounting standards.

6. A professional accounting organization whose members are certified public accountants (CPAs).

7. Issued official opinion on accounting standards between 1959-1973.

8. This board issues four types of pronouncements: (1) Statements of Financial Accounting Standards (SFAS), (2) Interpretations, (3) Technical bulletins, and (4) Statements of Financial Accounting Concepts (SFAC).

9. Presents all known facts and points of view on a topic. Issued by the FASB.

10. These statements are issued by the Financial Accounting Standards Board (FASB), and establish GAAP for specific accounting issues.

SOLUTION:

1.	j	6.	c
2.	a	7.	d
3.	i	8.	e
4.	b	9.	g
5.	h	10.	f

MULTIPLE CHOICE

c   1.   At the end of the fiscal year, an adjusting entry is
          made which increases both interest expense and interest
          payable. This entry is an application for which
          accounting principle?
          a.   full disclosure
          b.   materiality
          c.   matching
          d.   going concern
          e.   realization

b   2.   Who is responsible for the preparation and integrity of
          financial statements?
          a.   cost accountant
          b.   management
          c.   auditor
          d.   bookkeeper
          e.   FASB

b   3.   Which of the following is **not** an objective of the SEC's
          integrated disclosure system?
          a.   to coordinate the Form 10-K requirements with those
               of the annual report
          b.   to lessen the impact of the FASB
          c.   to expand the management discussion of liquidity,
               capital resources, and results of operations
          d.   improve the quality of disclosure
          e.   standardize information requirements

d   4.   Which of the following is **not** a type of audit opinion?
          a.   unqualified opinion
          b.   qualified opinion
          c.   adverse opinion
          d.   clean opinion
          e.   disclaimer of opinion

e 5. Which of the following statements is **not** true?

a. You are likely to regard a qualified opinion or an adverse opinion as a serious question of the reliability of the financial statements.

b. A disclaimer of opinion indicates that you should not look to the auditor's report as an indication of the reliability of the statements.

c. In some cases, outside accountants are associated with financial statements when they have performed less than an audit.

d. A review is substantially less in scope than an examination in accordance with generally accepted auditing statements.

e. The accountant's report expresses an opinion on reviewed financial statements.

c 6. In addition to a balance sheet, income statement and the statement of cash flows, a complete set of financial statements must include:

a. an auditor's opinion

b. a ten-year summary of operations

c. a footnote disclosure of such items as accounting policies

d. historical common-size (percentage) summaries

e. a list of corporate officers

d 7. Which of the following statements is **not** correct concerning summary annual reports.

a. A summary annual report omits much of the financial information included in an annual report.

b. When a company issues a summary annual report, the proxy materials it sends to shareholders must include a set of fully audited statements and other required financial disclosures.

c. A summary annual report generally has more non-financial pages than financial pages.

d. A summary annual report is adequate for reasonable analysis.

e. The concept of a summary annual report was approved by The Securities and Exchange Commission.

e   8. Which of the following would **not** be considered a
        subsequent event?
        a. A major customer declares bankruptcy subsequent to
            the balance sheet date but prior to issuing the
            statements. This event was not considered on the
            balance sheet date.
        b. A major purchase of a subsidiary subsequent to the
            balance sheet date but prior to issuing the
            statements.
        c. Substantial debt incurred subsequent to the balance
            sheet date but prior to issuing the statements.
        d. Substantial stock issued subsequent to the balance
            sheet date but prior to issuing the statements.
        e. Hiring of employees for a new store, subsequent to
            the balance sheet date but prior to issuing the
            statements.

e   9. Which of these statements is **not** true?
        a. Transactions must be recorded in a journal.
        b. All transactions could be recorded in the general
            journal.
        c. Companies use a number of special journals to record
            most transactions.
        d. Special journals are designed to improve record-
            keeping efficiency.
        e. The form of the journals are the same from indusry
            to industry.

e   10. Which of these statements is **not** true?
        a. Asset, liability, and stockholders' equity accounts
            are referred to as permanent accounts.
        b. Revenue, expense, and dividend accounts are
            described as temporary accounts.
        c. Temporary accounts are closed at the end of the
            period to retained earnings.
        d. The balance sheet will not balance until the
            temporary accounts are closed to retained earnings.
        e. With double-entry, each transaction is recorded
            twice.

TRUE/FALSE

T   1. Subsequent events are those that occur after the balance
        sheet date but before the statements are issued.

F   2. A disclaimer of opinion is necessary when the exceptions
        to fair presentation are so material that a qualified
        opinion is not justified.

T   3. The responsibility for the preparation and integrity of
        financial statements rests with management.

T   4. At any point in time, the assets for the balance sheet
        must equal the contribution of the creditors and owners.

2-3

F   5.   The retained earnings account is the link between the balance sheet and the statement of cash flows.

T   6.   A summary annual report is a condensed annual report that omits much of the financial information included in a typical annual report.

F   7.   A sole proprietorship is a legal entity separate from its owner.

T   8.   A partnership is a business owned by two or more individuals. Each owner is personally responsible for the debts of the partnership.

T   9.   A corporation is considered to be a legal entity separate and distinct from the stockholders.

T   10.   The principal financial statements of a corporation are the balance sheet, income statement, and statement of cash flows.

F   11.   A balance sheet shows the financial condition of an accounting entity for a particular period of time.

F   12.   At any point in time, assets must equal the contribution of the creditors.

T   13.   The income statement is a summary of revenues and expenses and gains and losses, ending with net income, for a particular period of time.

F   14.   Retained earnings links the balance sheet to the statement of cash flows.

T   15.   The statement of retained earnings reconciles the beginning retained earnings balance to the retained earnings balance at the end of the current period.

F   16.   The statement of cash flows consists of two sections: cash flows from operating activities and cash flows from financing activities.

F   17.   Contingent liabilities are recorded as a liability only if the loss is considered substantial and the amount is reasonably determinable.

T   18.   The sequence of accounting procedures completed during each accounting period is called the accounting cycle.

F   19.   Transactions must be external to the company.

T   20.   Accounts store the monetary information from the recording of transactions.

F   21.   T-accounts have a left (credit) side and a right (debit) side.

T   22.   Several accounts could be involved in a single transaction, but the debits and credits must still be equal.

T   23.   After posting, the general ledger accounts contain the same information as in the journals, but the information has been summarized by account.

F   24.   The point of cash receipt for revenue and cash disbursement for expenses is important under the accrual basis when determining income.

T   25.   The accrual basis needs numerous adjustments at the end of the accounting period.

F   26.   An adverse opinion states that, except for the effects of the matter(s) to which the qualification relates, the financial statements present fairly, in all material respects, the financial position, results of operations, and cash flows of the entity in conformity with generally accepted accounting principles.

T   27.   From the point of view of analysis, the unqualified opinion without an explanatory paragraph or explanatory language carries the highest degree of reliability.

F   28.   You are unlikely to regard a qualified opinion or an adverse opinion as casting serious doubts on the reliability of the financial statements.

T   29.   A review has substantially less scope than an examination in accordance with generally accepted auditing standards.

F   30.   The accountant's report expresses an opinion on reviewed financial statements.

T   31.   Sometimes financial statements are presented without an accompanying accountant's report.

F   32.   The responsibility for the preparation and integrity of financial statements rests with the auditors.

T   33.   The proxy is the solicitation sent to stockholders for the election of directors and for the approval of other corporation actions.

T   34.   In practice, much of the required information in the 10-K is incorporated by reference.

T   35.   A summary annual report generally has more non-financial pages than financial pages.

T   36.   Accepted accounting principles leave ample room for arriving at different results in the short run.

T   37.   Ethics can be a particular problem with financial reports.

F   38.   With the expansion of international business and global capital markets, the business community and governments have shown a decreased interest in the harmonization of international accounting standards.

T   39.   The IASC does not have authority to enforce its standards; but these standards have been adopted in whole or in part by many countries.

F   40.   Domestic accounting standards have developed to meet the needs of international environments.

F   41.   It is generally recognized that the market is more efficient when dealing with small firms that are not trading on large organized stock markets.

T   42.   The market will not be efficient if it does not have access to relevant information or if fraudulent information is provided.

T   43.   For consolidated statements, all transactions between entities being consolidated - intercompany transactions - must be eliminated.

F   44.   The financial statements of the parent and the subsidiary are consolidated for all subsidiaries unless control is temporary or does not rest with the majority.

T   45.   When a subsidiary is not consolidated, it is accounted for as an investment on the parent's balance sheet.

F   46.   There are three methods of accounting for a business combination.

F   47.   For a business combination, the pooling method results in the acquired assets and liabilities being carried forward at the amount that they were previously recorded. This results in a net overstatement of assets, liabilities, and owners' equity in relation to the acquisition values.

T   48.   For a business combination, the purchase method views the business combination as the acquisition of one entity by another. The firm doing the acquiring records

T   49.   Conceptually, accumulated other comprehensive income represents retained earnings from other comprehensive income.

PROBLEMS

1.

The following are selected accounts and account balances of the Gorr Company on December 31:

	Permanent (P) or Temporary (T)	Normal Balance Dr. (Cr.)
Inventory		
Land		
Wages Payable		
Capital Stock		
Retained Earnings		
Revenues		
Dividends		
Advertising Expense		

Required:
a.   Indicate if the account is a permanent (P) or temporary (T) account.
b.   Indicate the normal balance in terms of debit (Dr) or credit (Cr).

SOLUTION:

	Permanent (P) or Temporary (T)	Normal Balance Dr (Cr)
Inventory	P	Dr
Land	P	Dr
Wages Payable	P	Cr
Capital Stock	P	Cr
Retained Earnings	P	Cr
Revenues	T	Cr
Dividends	T	Dr
Advertising Expense	T	Dr

2.

Listed below are several accounts or statement categories.

	Balance Sheet (BS)
	Income Statement (IS)
Account or Statement Category	Statement of Cash Flows (SCF

Accounts Receivable
Inventory
Prepaid Insurance
Sales
Cost of Goods Sold
Cash Flow from Investing Activities
Notes Payable
Interest Expense
Tax Expense
Taxes Payable
Administrative Expense
Current Assets
Advertising Expense
Cash Flow from Financing Activities

Required:

In the space provided indicate the financial statement as balance sheet (BS), income statement (IS) or statement of cash flows (SCF).

SOLUTION:

	Balance Sheet (BS)
	Income Statement (IS)
Account or Statement Category	Statement of Cash Flows (SCF
Accounts Receivable	BS
Inventory	BS
Prepaid Insurance	BS
Sales	IS
Cost of Goods Sold	IS
Cash Flow from Investing Activities	SCF
Notes Payable	BS
Interest Expense	IS
Tax Expense	IS
Taxes Payable	BS
Administrative Expense	IS
Current Assets	BS
Advertising Expense	IS
Cash Flow from Financing Activities	SCF

3.

Listed below is information related to several adjusting entry situations. Assume that the accounting year ends on December 31.

1. $3,000 paid for insurance on October 1 for a one-year period (October 1 - September 30). This transaction was recorded as a debit to prepaid insurance ($3,000) and a credit to cash ($3,000).

2. Interest on bonds payable in the amount of $500 has not been recorded at December 31.

3. Rent expense in he amount of $1,200 was paid on November 1. This transaction was recorded as a debit to rent expense $1,200) and a credit to cash ($1,200). This rent payment was for the period November 1 - January 31.

Required:

Record the original entries and the adjusting entries using T-accounts.

SOLUTION:

Prepaid Insurance			
10-1	3,000	12-31	750

Cash			
		10-1	3,000
		11-1	1,200

Insurance Expense			
1-31	750		

Interest Expense			
12-31	500		

Interest Payable			
		12-31	500

Prepaid Rent			
12-31	400		

Rent Expense			
11-1	1,200	12-31	400

Chapter 3: BALANCE SHEET

MULTIPLE CHOICE

e   1. The balance sheet reports:
    a. the assets, liabilities, gains, and losses for a period of time
    b. the changes in assets, liabilities, and equity for a period of time
    c. the assets, expenses, and liabilities as of a certain date
    d. the probable future benefits, probable future sacrifices, and residual interest for a period of time
    e. the financial condition of an accounting entity as of a particular date

b   2. Which of the following would **not** appear on a conventional balance sheet?
    a. income taxes payable
    b. funds from operations
    c. cash surrender value of life insurance
    d. appropriation for contingencies (restriction of retained earnings)
    e. patents

d   3. Execon Company had total assets of $200,000, total liabilities of $110,000, and shareholders' equity of $90,000 at the beginning of the year. For the year, Execon Company earned net income of $75,000 and declared cash dividends of $30,000. At the end of the year, the company had total assets of $300,000 and its shareholders' equity was at $135,000. At the end of the year, Execon Corporation had total liabilities of:
    a. $ 0
    b. $ 45,000
    c. $ 50,000
    d. $165,000
    e. none of the above

c   4. Ownership and debt instruments of the government and other companies that can be readily converted to cash are best reported as:
    a. long-term investments
    b. cash
    c. marketable securities
    d. intangibles
    e. inventory of near-cash items

a   5.   Tangible assets on the balance sheet should include:
         a.   equipment
         b.   taxes payable
         c.   trademarks
         d.   bonds payable
         e.   none of the above

e   6.   The current asset section of the balance sheet should
         include:
         a.   land
         b.   trademarks
         c.   investment in C Company (for purposes of control)
         d.   dividends payable
         e.   work in process inventory

d   7.   The current liability section of the balance sheet
         should include:
         a.   buildings
         b.   goodwill
         c.   land held for speculation purposes
         d.   accounts payable
         e.   none of the above

c   8.   Which of the following is **not** a current asset?
         a.   marketable securities
         b.   material inventory
         c.   unearned rent income
         d.   prepaid interest
         e.   prepaid insurance

b   9.   If a parent has some control over a subsidiary but the
         subsidiary is not consolidated, the subsidiary is
         accounted for as a(an):
         a.   marketable security
         b.   investment
         c.   liability
         d.   fixed asset
         e.   none of the above

d   10. Which of the following is **not** a proper use of
         footnotes?
         a.   to describe the nature and effect of a change in
              accounting principle, such as from fifo to lifo
         b.   to indicate the basis for asset valuation
         c.   to indicate the method of depreciation
         d.   to correct an improper financial statement
              presentation
         e.   to describe a firm's debt

d (11) Company A owns shares of Companies B and C. The statements of Company B are consolidated with those of A. The statements of Company C are not consolidated. Company A reports "Minority Interest" on its balance sheet. This account represents:

   a. A's minority share of the stock of B
   b. A's minority share of the stock of C
   c. the minority share by outside owners of the stock of A
   d. the minority share by outside owners of the stock of B
   e. the minority share by outside owners of the stock of C

c (12.) Drama Products Inc. has issued redeemable preferred stock. For analysis purposes, these securities are best classified as:

   a. marketable securities
   b. long-term investments
   c. long-term debt
   d. paid-in capital
   e. retained earnings

d 13. Treasury stock is best classified as:

   a. a current asset
   b. a long-term investment
   c. a contra liability
   d. a reduction of stockholders' equity
   e. a reduction of retained earnings

a (14.) Which of the following is **not** a common characteristic of preferred stock?

   a. voting rights
   b. preference as to dividends
   c. preference in liquidation
   d. callability by the corporation
   e. none of the above

e (15.) Which of the following is **not** a problem inherent in balance sheet presentation?

   a. Most assets are valued at cost.
   b. Varying methods are used for asset valuation.
   c. Not all items of value to the firm are included as assets.
   d. Liabilities related to contingencies may not appear on the balance sheet.
   e. The owners' interest will be indicated.

e   16.   Which of the following is **not** true relating to
           treasury stock?
           a.   A firm creates treasury stock when it repurchases
                its own stock and does not retire it.
           b.   Treasury stock lowers the stock outstanding.
           c.   Treasury stock may be recorded at the cost of the
                stock.
           d.   Treasury stock may be recorded at par or stated
                value.
           e.   Treasury stock is, in essence, an increase in
                paid-in capital.

a   17.   Which of the following is **not** true about an ESOP?
           a.   An ESOP will reduce the amount of voting stock in
                the hands of employees.
           b.   An ESOP must be a permanent trusted plan for the
                exclusive benefit of the employees.
           c.   The plan participants become eligible for
                favorable taxation of distributions from the plan.
           d.   Commercial lending institutions, insurance
                companies, and mutual funds are permitted an
                exclusion from income for 5% of the interest
                received on loans used to finance an ESOP's
                acquisition of company stock.
           e.   An ESOP may reduce the potential of an unfriendly
                takeover.

d   18.   The most popular depreciation method for financial
           reporting is the following:
           a.   units-of-production
           b.   sum-of-the-years-digits
           c.   declining-balance
           d.   straight-line
           e.   other

TRUE/FALSE

F   1.   The purpose of a balance sheet is to show the
           financial condition of an accounting entity for a
           period of time.

T   2.   In a period of rising prices, lifo usually results in
           a realistic cost of goods sold.

F   3.   Generally accepted accounting principles and the
           Internal Revenue Code of tax law require that the same
           depreciation method be used for both the financial
           statements and the federal tax return.

F   4.   All intangibles are amortized over their useful lives
           or their legal lives, whichever is shorter.

T   (5.)   Deferred taxes are caused by using different accounting methods for tax and financial reporting purposes.

T   (6.)   Assets are probable future economic benefits obtained or controlled by an entity as a result of past transactions or events.

T   (7.)   Minority interest reflects the ownership of minority shareholders in the equity of consolidated subsidiaries that are less than wholly owned.

F   (8.)   The stockholders' equity section of the balance sheet includes redeemable preferred stock.

F   (9.)   When a firm repurchases its own stock and retires it, the stock is called treasury stock.

T   10.   A sole proprietorship form of business has only one owner.

F   11.   The financial statements of legally separate entities may be issued to show the financial position and income as they would appear if the companies were one legal entity. Such statements reflect a legal, rather than an economic, concept of the entity.

T   (12).   Current assets are listed on the balance sheet in order of liquidity.

T   (13.)   Long-term investments, usually stocks and bonds of other companies, are often held to maintain a business relationship or exercise control.

T   14.   When preferred stock has a preference as to dividends, the current year's preferred dividend must be paid before a dividend can be paid to common stockholders.

F   15.   If dividends are not declared by the board of directors in a particular year, a holder of cumulative preferred stock will never be paid that dividend.

F   16.   Preferred stock usually has voting rights.

T   (17.)   Warranty obligations are estimated in order to recognize the obligation at the balance sheet date and to charge the expense to the period of the sale.

T   18.   Corporations do not use a standard title for owners' equity.

T   19.   A quasi-reorganization is an accounting procedure equivalent to an accounting fresh start.

T   20.   Our current FASB covering foreign currency translation
          eliminates the wide fluctuations in earnings from
          translation adjustments for most firms.

T   21.   The deferred compensation element of an equity-based
          deferred compensation arrangement is the amount of
          compensation cost deferred and amortized (expensed) to
          future periods as the services are provided.

F   22.   An ESOP is a qualified stock-bonus or combination
          stock-bonus and money-purchase pension plan designed
          to invest primarily in stock, other than the
          employer's securities.

F   23.   The Internal Revenue Code penalizes borrowing for an
          ESOP.

PROBLEMS

1. Assume that Eugene Motor Corp. uses the following headings
on its balance sheet:

A. Current Assets
B. Investments
C. Property, Plant, and
   Equipment
D. Intangible Assets
E. Current Liabilities

F. Long-Term
   Liabilities
G. Capital Stock
H. Retained Earnings
I. Stockholders'
   Equity

Required:
Indicate by letter how each of the following should be best
classified. If an item would not appear on the balance sheet but
would appear in a footnote to the financial statements, use the
letter "N" to indicate this fact. If an item is neither reported
on the balance sheet nor disclosed as a footnote, use the letter
"X". If the account balance is normally opposite that of a
typical account in that classification, indicate this by placing
the letter in parentheses, ( ).

a.	Patents	n.	Unamortized Bond Payable Discount (bonds due in 5 years)
b.	Merchandise Inventory		
c.	Taxes Payable	o.	Receivable from Officer-due in 6 months
d.	Employee Payroll Deduction for State Income Taxes		
		p.	Accumulated Deficit (losses incurred since inception)
e.	Cash		
f.	Office Supplies	q.	Insurance Expense
g.	Preferred Stock	r.	Goodwill
h.	Common Stock	s.	Interest Accrued on U.S. Government Securities Owned
i.	Work in Process		
j.	Land	t.	Accounts payable
k.	Accounts Receivable	u.	Treasury Stock
l.	Accumulated Depreciation	v.	Wages Payable
m.	Unearned Rent Income	w.	Land Purchased as Future Development Site
		x.	Unexpired Rent Expense (prepaid rent)

SOLUTION:

a.	D	f.	A	k.	A	p.	(H)	u.	(I)
b.	A	g.	G	l.	(C)	q.	X	v.	E
c	E	h.	G	m.	E	r.	D	w.	B
d	E	i.	A	n.	(F)	s.	A	x.	A
e	A	j.	C	o.	A	t.	E		

2.

Required:
Using the letters provided, classify items (1-13) according to the most commonly preferred balance sheet presentation.

Assets	Liabilities and Stockholders' Equity
a. Current Assets b. Tangible Assets c. Investments d. Intangibles e. Other	f. Current Liability g. Long-Term Liability h. Capital Stock i. Retained Earnings j. Items Not Included on Balance Sheet

1. Land
2. Marketable Securities
3. Goodwill
4. Inventories
5. Premium on Preferred Stock
6. Appropriation for Expansion
7. Depreciation Expense
8. Investment in K Company Bonds (long-term investment)
9. Accounts Payable
10. Bonds Payable
11. Equipment
12. Copyright
13. Unamortized Premium on Bonds Payable

SOLUTION:

1.	b	7.	j	13.	g
2.	a	8.	c		
3.	d	9.	f		
4.	a	10.	g		
5.	h	11.	b		
6.	i	12.	d		

3.

A partial list of accounts for Johnson and Clark, in alphabetical order, is presented below:

Accounts Payable
Accounts Receivable
Accrued Salaries Payable
Accumulated Depreciation - Buildings
Accumulated Depreciation - Equipment
Additional Paid-In Capital - Common Stock
Allowance for Doubtful Accounts
Bank Loan (long-term)
Bonds Payable
Buildings
Cash in Bank
Commission Expense
Common Stock
Current Portion of Long-Term Debt
Equipment

FICA Taxes Payable
Franchise
Goodwill
Interest Income
Interest Receivable
Inventory - Ending Balance
Land
Land Held for Future Plant Site
Loss on Sale of Equipment
Marketable Securities
Minority Interest
Notes Payable (long-term)
Obligations on Long-Term Loans
Patent
Preferred Stock
Premium on Bonds Payable
Prepaid Expenses
Purchases
Retained Earnings
Sales
Sales Salaries Expense
Treasury Stock
Unearned Rent Income

Required:
Prepare a balance sheet in good format, without monetary amounts,
for December 31, 19XX. Use the format Current Assets,Property,
Plant, and Equipment, Investments, Intangibles, Current
Liabilities, Long-Term Liabilities, Stockholders' Equity. Do not
use the accounts not found on the balance sheet.

SOLUTION:

Johnson and Clark
Balance Sheet
December 31, 19XX

Assets
Current Assets:
      Cash in Bank
      Marketable Securities
      Accounts Receivable
      Less: Allowance for Doubtful Accounts
      Interest Receivable
      Inventory (ending balance)
      Prepaid Expenses
Property, Plant, and Equipment
      Land
      Buildings
      Less: Accumulated Depreciation—Buildings
      Equipment
      Less: Accumulated Depreciation—Equipment
Investments:
      Land Held for Future Plant Site
Intangibles:
      Franchise
      Patent
      Goodwill
        Total Assets

Liabilities and Stockholders' Equity
Current Liabilities:
      Accounts Payable
      Accrued Salaries Payable
      FICA Taxes Payable
      Unearned Rent Income
      Current Portion of Long-Term Debt
        Total Current Liabilities
Long-Term Liabilities:
      Bonds Payable
      Plus: Premium on Bonds Payable
      Notes Payable—Long-Term
      Bank Loan—Long-Term
      Obligations on Long-Term Loans
      Minority Interest
Stockholders' Equity:
      Preferred Stock
      Common Stock
      Additional Paid-In Capital - Common Stock
      Retained Earnings
      Less: Treasury Stock
        Total Liabilities and Stockholders' Equity

4.

The following is a partial listing of accounts for Euisara, Inc., for the year ended December 31, 2000.

Required:
Prepare a balance sheet in good format for December 31, 2000.

Finished Goods	$ 9,718
Current Maturities of Long-Term Debt	1,257
Accumulated Depreciation	9,980
Accounts Receivable	24,190
Sales Revenue	127,260
Treasury Stock	251
Prepaid Expenses	2,199
Deferred Taxes (long-term liability)	8,506
Interest Expense	2,410
Allowance for Doubtful Accounts	915
Retained Earnings	18,951
Raw Materials	9,576
Accounts payable	19,021
Cash and Cash Equivalents	8,527
Sales Salaries Expense	872
Cost of Goods Sold	82,471
Investment in Unconsolidated Subsidiaries	3,559
Income Taxes Payable	8,356
Work In Process	1,984
Additional Paid-In Capital	9,614
Equipment	41,905
Long-Term Debt	15,258
Rent Income	2,468
Common Stock	3,895
Notes Payable (short-term)	6,156
Income Tax Expense	2,461

SOLUTION:

Euisara, Inc.
Balance Sheet
December 31, 2000

<u>Assets</u>
Current Assets:

Cash and Cash Equivalents		$ 8,527	
Accounts Receivable	$ 24,190		
Less: Allowance for Doubtful Accounts	(915)	23,275	
Inventories:			
Raw Materials	$ 9,576		
Work In Process	1,984		
Finished Goods	9,718	21,278	
Prepaid Expenses		2,199	
Total Current Assets			$ 55,279

Tangible Assets:		
Equipment	$ 41,905	
Less: Accumulated Depreciation	(9,980)	31,925
Investments:		
Investments in Unconsolidated Subsidiaries		3,559
Total Assets		$ 90,763

<u>Liabilities and Stockholders' Equity</u>
Current Liabilities:

Current Maturities of Long-Term Debt	$ 1,257	
Notes Payable	6,156	
Accounts Payable	19,021	
Income Taxes Payable	8,356	
Total Current Liabilities		$ 34,790

Long-Term Liabilities:		
Long-Term Debt	15,258	
Deferred Taxes	8,506	
Total Long-Term Liabilities		23,764

Stockholders' Equity:		
Common Stock	$ 3,895	
Additional Paid-In Capital	9,614	
Retained Earnings	18,951	
	32,460	
Less: Treasury Stock	(251)	32,209
Total Liabilities and Stockholders' Equity		$90,763

5.

The following balance sheet, prepared by a careless bookkeeper, has been given to you to review.

Required:
List any types of corrections that need to be made. Errors can be in classification, lack of disclosure, format, or terminology.

Eldorado, Inc.
Balance Sheet
For the Year Ended June 30, 2000

Assets

Current Assets:		
Accounts Receivable	$ 37,000	
Merchandise Inventory	62,000	
Cash	17,000	$ 116,000
Investments:		
Marketable Securities	$ 18,000	
Treasury Stock	4,000	22,000
Tangible Assets:		
Buildings	$ 194,000	
Less: Reserve for Depreciation	(34,000)	160,000
Other Assets:		
Unamortized Portion of Bond		
Payable Discount		3,000
		$ 301,000

Liabilities and Stockholders' Equity

Current Liabilities:		
Accounts Payable	$ 26,000	
Bank Note Payable		
(due 6/1/2000)	22,000	$ 48,000
Long-term Liabilities:		
Bonds Payable		112,000
Capital Stock:		
Common Stock	$ 49,000	
Earned Surplus	92,000	
		141,000
		$ 301,000

SOLUTION:
1. The date should read "June 30, 2000," as a balance sheet is at a particular point in time.
2. Cash should be listed first under current assets.
3. Marketable securities should be a current asset, listed after cash.

4. Treasury stock should be deducted from stockholders' equity.
5. "Allowance" is a better term than "Reserve" in relation to depreciation.
6. The bond discount should be subtracted from bonds payable rather than being shown as an asset.
7. The bank note payable is not due within a year and should be classified as long-term.
8. Retained earnings is now common terminology to replace earned surplus.
9. The method of valuation of marketable securities should be disclosed.
10. The inventory costing method should be disclosed.
11. The maturity date and interest rate of the bonds should be disclosed.
12. The par value and number of shares should be disclosed for the stock.

6.

The following balance sheet, prepared by Whoops Bookkeeping Service, has been given to you to review.

Required:
Prepare a corrected, properly classified balance sheet in report form.

Butler Corporation
Balance Sheet
For Year Ended December 31, 2000

Current Assets:		Current Liabilities:	
Cash	$ 6,200	Accounts Payable	$ 15,000
Accounts Receivable	13,000	Wages Payable	2,000
Inventory	30,000	Accumulated Deprecia-	
Treasury Stock	10,000	tion - Equipment	5,000
		Accumulated Deprecia-	
Property, Plant, and Equipment:		tion - Buildings	10,000
Land	7,000		
Trademarks	5,000	Long-Term Liabilities:	
Buildings	45,000	Current Taxes Payable	4,000
Equipment	17,000	Premium on Common Stock	3,000
Intangibles		Bonds Payable	60,000
Organization Costs	4,000	Notes Payable—Long	
Discount on Bonds		Term	10,000
Payable	2,000		
		Owners' Equity:	
Investments:		Common Stock	31,200
Long-Term Investment		Retained Earnings	12,000
in Bonds	8,000	Allowance for Doubtful	
Marketable Securities-		Accounts	
Short-Term	7,000		2,000
Total Assets	$154,200		$154,200

```
                     Butler Corporation
                       Balance Sheet
                    December 31, 2000

Assets
Current Assets:
  Cash                                            $ 6,200
  Marketable securities                             7,000
  Accounts receivable             $13,000
  Less: Allowance for doubtful
     accounts                      (2,000)         11,000
  Inventory                                        30,000
      Total current assets                                   $ 54,200

Tangible Assets:
  Land                                            $ 7,000
  Equipment                       $17,000
  Less: Accumulated depreciation   (5,000)         12,000
  Buildings                        45,000
  Less: Accumulated depreciation
     buildings                    (10,000)         35,000         54,000

Investments:
  Investment in bonds                                              8,000

Intangibles:
  Trademarks                                      $ 5,000
  Organization costs                                4,000          9,000
Total assets                                                    $125,200

Liabilities and Stockholders' Equity
Current Liabilities:
  Accounts payable                                $15,000
  Wages payable                                     2,000
  Current taxes payable                             4,000
     Total current liabilities                               $ 21,000

Long-Term Debt:
  Notes payable - long-term                       $10,000
  Bonds payable                   $60,000
  Less: Discount on bonds payable  (2,000)         58,000
     Total long-term debt                                        68,000

Owners' Equity:
  Common stock                                     31,200
  Premium on common stock                           3,000
  Retained earnings                                12,000
  Treasury stock                                  (10,000)        36,200
Total liabilities and stockholders' equity                     $125,200
```

7.

Required:
Using the information given below, prepare a classified balance
sheet in good form for the Babic Company at December 31, 2000.

Accounts Payable	$ 83,000
Accounts Receivable	109,000
Accrued Liabilities	22,000
Accumulated Depreciation	326,000
Cash	32,000
Common Stock	107,000
Convertible Debentures	464,000
Deferred Income Taxes (Long-Term Liability)	117,000
Equipment	1,070,000
Inventory	146,000
Land	917,000
Marketable Securities	11,000
Minority Interest	97,000
Paid-In Capital in Excess of Par	141,000
Retained Earnings	952,000
Treasury Stock	24,000

SOLUTION:

Babic Company
Balance Sheet
December 31, 2000
Assets

Current Assets:

Cash		$ 32,000	
Marketable Securities		11,000	
Accounts Receivable		109,000	
Inventory		146,000	
Total Current Assets		$ 298,000	

Tangible Assets:

Land		$ 917,000	
Equipment	$1,070,000		
Less: Accumulated Depreciation	(326,000)	744,000	1,661,000
Total Assets			$1,959,000

Liabilities and Stockholders' Equity

Current Liabilities:
Accounts Payable	$ 83,000	
Accrued Liabilities	22,000	
Total Current Liabilities		$ 105,000
Convertible Debentures		464,000
Deferred Income Taxes		117,000
Minority Interest		97,000

Stockholders' Equity
Common Stock	$ 107,000	
Paid-In Capital in Excess of Par	141,000	
Retained Earnings	952,000	
	$ 1,200,000	
Less: Treasury Stock Required:	(24,000)	1,176,000
Total Liabilities and Stockholders' Equity		$1,959,000

8.

Required:
Match each account to the proper account description by placing the appropriate letter before the account name.

Account

1. Accounts Payable
2. Accounts Receivable
3. Accrued Liabilities
4. Accumulated Depreciation
5. Cash
6. Common Stock
7. Convertible Debentures
8. Deferred Income Taxes (liability)
9. Equipment
10. Inventory
11. Land
12. Marketable Securities
13. Minority Interest
14. Paid-In Capital in Excess of Par
15. Retained Earnings
16. Treasury Stock

Account Descriptions

a. Stocks and bonds of other companies held for the purpose of exercising control.
b. An accumulation of the sum of the expense since the beginning of the benefit period.

c. Outside ownership in the equity of consolidated subsidiaries.
d. Machinery and tools, valued at historical cost.
e. Monies due because expenses, such as salaries, are incurred in a different period than when the cash outlay occurs.
f. The most liquid of assets, it may also include savings accounts.
g. Goods on hand.
h. A potential liability created by differing tax and reporting methods.
i. Ownership and debt instruments readily converted to cash.
j. An expenditure made in advance of the use of the service or good.
k. Monies due from customers arising from sale or service rendered.
l. The capital stock of residual owners.
m. Bonds that can be exchanged for stock at the option of the holder.
n. Undistributed earnings of the corporation
o. Shares of the firm's own stock that have been repurchased.
p. Monies due for goods bought for use or resale.
q. Excess over legal par paid at time of sale.
r. Non-depreciable real estate.
s. Collections in advance of service.
t. Securities that give the holder the right to buy additional shares of common stock at a fixed price.

SOLUTION:

1.	p	9.	d
2.	k	10.	g
3.	e	11.	r
4.	b	12.	i
5.	f	13.	c
6.	l	14.	q
7.	m	15.	n
8.	h	16.	o

Account Descriptions a, j, s, and t are not used.

9.

An item of equipment acquired on January 1 at a cost of $100,000 has an estimated use of 50,000 hours. During the first three years, the equipment was used 11,000, 8,000, and 7,000 hours, respectively. The equipment has an estimated life of five years and an estimated salvage of $10,000.

Required:
Determine the depreciation for each of the three years, using the straight-line method, the declining-balance method, the sum-of-the-years'-digits method, and the unit-of-production method.

SOLUTION:

Straight-Line: = $18,000 Each Year
                          5

Declining-Balance =
    Year 1:
        1/5 x 2 x $100,000 = $40,000 1st Year
    Year 2:
        1/5 x 2 x ($100,000-$40,000) = $24,000 2nd Year
    Year 3:
        1/5 x 2 x ($100,000-$64,000) = $14,400 3rd Year

Sum-Of-The-Years'-Digits:
    Year 1:
        5/15 x ($100,000-$10,000) = $30,000
    Year 2:
        4/15 x ($100,000-$10,000) = $24,000
    Year 3:
        3/15 x ($100,000-$10,000) = $18,000

Unit-Of-Production Method:

                        = $1.80
            50,000

    Year 1:
            11,000 x $1.80 = $19,800
    Year 2:
            8,000 x $1.80 = $14,400
    Year 3:
            7,000 x $1.80 = $12,600

10.

Szabo Company has had 10,000 shares of 8%, $100 par-value preferred stock and 15,000 shares of $10 par-value common stock outstanding for the last two years. During the most recent year, dividends paid totaled $100,000; in the prior year, dividends paid totaled $60,000.

Required: Compute the amount of dividends that must have been paid to preferred stockholders and common stockholders in each of the years, given the following independent assumptions:

a.   Preferred stock is nonparticipating and noncumulative.
b.   Preferred stock is nonparticipating and cumulative.

SOLUTION:

a.

	Preferred Stock	Common Stock
Year 1 Dividends, $60,000		
Preferred Stock 10,000 x $100 x 8% = $80,000	$ 60,000	--0--
Year 2 Dividends, $100,000		
Preferred Stock 10,000 x $100 x 8% = $80,000	$ 80,000	$20,000

b.

	Preferred Stock	Common Stock
Year 1 Dividends, $60,000		
Preferred Stock 10,000 x $100 x 8% = $80,000	$ 60,000	--0--
Year 2 Dividends, $100,000		
Preferred Stock Carryover from year 1	$ 20,000	
10,000 x $100 x 8% = $80,000	80,000	--0--
	$100,000	

Chapter 4: INCOME STATEMENT

MULTIPLE CHOICE

c 1. Gross profit is the difference between:
   a. net income and operating income
   b. revenues and expenses
   c. sales and cost of goods sold
   d. income from continuing operations and discontinued operations
   e. gross sales and sales discounts

b 2. Which of the following would be included in operating income?
   a. interest income for a manufacturing firm
   b. rent income for a leasing subsidiary
   c. gain from sale of marketable securities for a retailer
   d. dividend income for a service firm
   e. none of the above

a 3. The following relate to Data Original in 19XX. What is the ending inventory?

Purchases	$540,000
Beginning Inventory	80,000
Purchase returns	10,000
Sales	800,000
Cost of goods sold	490,000

   a. $120,000
   b. $140,000
   c. $210,000
   d. $260,000
   e. none of the above

c 4. Changes in account balances of Multi-Plus, Inc. during 2000 were:

	Increase
Assets	$420,000
Liabilities	125,000
Capital stock	100,000
Additional paid-in capital	140,000
Retained earnings	?

   Assuming that there were no charges to retained earnings other than dividends of $62,000, the net income for 2000 was:
   a. ($7,000)
   b. $55,000
   c. $117,000
   d. $257,000
   e. none of the above

e 5. When a company discontinues and disposes of a segment of
its operations, the gain or loss from disposal should be
reported as:
a. an adjustment to retained earnings
b. a sale of fixed assets in "other" expense
c. an extraordinary item
d. an accounting change
e. a special item after continuing operations and
before extraordinary items

c 6. If the disposal of a segment meets the criteria of APB
Opinion No. 30, then:
a. the loss on disposal is an extraordinary item
b. the loss on disposal is categorized as "other
expense"
c. the results of operations of the segment will be
reported in conjunction with the gain or loss on
disposal
d. the disposal qualifies as a change in entity, and
prior years' statements presented on comparative
purposes must be restated
e. the effects of the disposal are shown as part of
operations

e 7. Which of the following would be classified as an
extraordinary item on the income statement?
a. loss from a strike
b. correction of an error related to a prior period
c. write-off of obsolete inventory
d. loss on disposal of a segment of business
e. loss from prohibition of a product

b 8. If a firm consolidates subsidiaries that are not wholly
owned, an income statement item is created that is
termed:
a. dividend income
b. minority share of earnings
    c.   equity income
d. extraordinary
e. gain from sale of subsidiary

b 9. Which of the following will **not** affect retained
earnings?
a. declaration of a stock dividend
b. payment of a cash dividend previously disclosed
c. adjustment for an error of a prior period
d. net income
e. net loss

e 10. Anchor Company has 1,000,000 shares of common stock with
       par of $5. Additional paid-in capital totals $5,000,000
       and retained earnings is $8,000,000. The directors
       declare a 10% stock dividend when the market value is
       $15. The reduction of retained earnings as a result of
       the declaration will be:
       a. $0
       b. $500,000
       c. $800,000
       d. $1,000,000
       e. $1,500,000

c 11. The stockholders' equity of Anamanda Company at
       September 30, 2001, is presented below:

       Common Stock, par value $10, authorized
       500,000 shares;
       200,000 shares issued and outstanding $2,000,000
       Paid-In Capital in Excess of Par   300,000
       Retained Earnings   1,300,000
                                                       $3,600,000

       On October 1, 2001, the Board of Directors of Anamanda
       declared a 10% stock dividend to be distributed on
       November 10. The market price of the common stock was
       $15 on October 1 and $17 on November 10. What is the
       amount of the charge to retained earnings as a result of
       the declaration and distribution of this stock dividend?
       a. $0
       b. $200,000
       c. $300,000
       d. $340,000
       e. $750,000

d 12. Andromeda Industries had 300,000 shares of common stock
       with a $3 par value and retained earnings of $180,000.
       In 2000, earnings per share were $1.80. In 2001, the
       stock was split 3 for 1. Which of the following would
       not result from the stock split?
       a. The new shares would total 900,000.
       b. The total amount in the capital stock account would
           remain the same.
       c. The par value would become $1.
       d. Retained earnings would be reduced.
       e. The earnings per share for 2000 would be restated at
           $.60.

e   13. Which of the following is **not** true about a stock
          dividend?
          a. With a stock dividend, the firm issues a percentage
              of outstanding stock as new shares to existing
              shareholders.
          b. The overall effect of a stock dividend is to leave
              total stockholders' equity and each owner's share of
              stockholders' equity unchanged.
          c. With a stock dividend, total market value
              considering all outstanding shares should not
              change.
          d. Since the number of shares changes under a stock
              dividend, any ratio based on the number of shares
              must be restated.
          e. The accounting for a stock dividend, assuming the
              distribution is relatively small, requires that the
              par value of the stock be removed from retained
              earnings.

a   14. Which of the following is **not** a category within
          accumulated other comprehensive income?
          a. Post retirement commitments on health plans.
          b. Foreign currency translation adjustments.
          c. Unrealized holding gains and losses on available-
              for-sale marketable securities.
          d. Changes to stockholders equity resulting from
              additional minimum pension liability adjustments.
          e. Unrealized gains and losses from derivative
              instruments.

TRUE/FALSE

F   1.   In practice, the income statement is frequently
          considered to be the least important financial
          statement.

F   2.   Gross profit will be a prominent figure on a single-step
          income statement.

T   3.   An income statement is a summary of revenues and
          expenses and gains and losses, ending with net income
          for a particular period of time.

F   4.   Advertising expense would be an administrative expense.

T   5.   Other income and other expense are categories under
          which secondary activities of the firm not directly
          related to the operations are classified.

T   6.   The term primary analysis is used to describe consistent
          and conservative analysis.

T   7.   Equity earnings can distort the success of a business in
          its operations other than investing in other companies.

T   8.   Ideally, income from continuing operations would be the better income figure to use to project the future from the analysis of historical statements.

F   9.   In analysis of income for purposes of determining a trend, extraordinary items should be included.

F   10.   Extraordinary items are always presented gross of applicable income taxes.

F   11.   Changes in accounting principles always require retroactive adjustments to reflect the new accounting principle.

T   12.   Earnings per share is the earnings per share of outstanding common stock.

T   13.   Presenting an item after tax, with the related tax deducted, is called net-of-tax presentation.

T   14.   Equity earnings (losses) are the proportionate share of the earnings (losses) of the investee.

T   15.   It is the date of the declaration of dividends that affects retained earnings and creates the liability, not the date of dividend payment.

F   16.   With a stock dividend, total market value considering all outstanding shares should decline.

T   17.   A stock split merely increases the number of shares of stock; it does not usually change retained earnings or paid-in capital.

F   18.   The legality of distributions to stockholders is governed by federal law.

T   19.   Accountants have not accepted the role of disclosing the firms capacity to make distributions to stockholders.

T   20.   Comprehensive income is net income plus the periods change in accumulated other comprehensive income.

PROBLEMS

1.

Required: Indicate the section of a multiple-step income statement in which each of the following items would usually appear for a manufacturing company.

a.   fire loss, net of tax
b.   depreciation on office equipment
c.   interest income

d. sales commissions
e. cost of goods manufactured
f. dividend income
g. advertising expense
h. interest expense
i. factory workers' salaries

SOLUTION:

a. extraordinary items
b. administrative or general expenses
c. other income
d. selling expense
e. cost of goods sold
f. other income
g. selling expense
h. other expense
i. cost of goods sold

2.

Information related to Batavia Furniture Company for the year
ended December 31, 2000, follows.

Cost of Goods Sold	$ 70,000
Dividends Declared	5,000
Flood Loss (pre-tax)	12,000
General Expense	8,000
Other Income	9,000
Other Expense	11,000
Retained Earnings, January 1, 2000	116,000
Sales	131,000
Selling Expense	7,000

Required:
Prepare in good form a multiple-step income statement for the
year 2000. Assume a 50% tax rate and that 5,000 shares of common
stock were outstanding during the year.

SOLUTION:

Batavia Furniture Company
Income Statement
For the Year Ended December 31, 2000

Sales		$131,000
Cost of Goods Sold		70,000
Gross Profit		61,000
Operating Expenses		
Selling Expenses	$7,000	
General Expenses	8,000	
		15,000
Operating Income		46,000
Other Income		9,000
Other Expense		(11,000)
Income Before Tax		44,000
Income Tax		22,000
Income Before Extraordinary Items		22,000
Flood Loss, Net of $6,000 Tax		6,000
Net Income		$ 16,000

Per Share of Common Stock:	
Income Before Extraordinary Item	$4.40
Extraordinary Item	(1.20)
Net Income	$3.20

3.

The income statement for Lifeline Products in single-step format
follows.

Lifeline Products
Income Statement
For the Year Ended December 31, 2000

Revenues:	
Sales	$3,000,000
Rent Income	14,000
	3,014,000
Costs and Expenses:	
Cost of Sales	2,370,000
Selling and Administrative Expenses	322,000
Interest Expense	48,000
Loss on the Sale of Plant Assets	16,000
	2,756,000
Income Before Taxes	258,000
Income Taxes	112,000
Net Income	$ 146,000
Earnings Per Share	$7.30

Required:
a. Convert the statement to multiple-step format.
b. Recompute net income with the unusual loss removed.

c.   Why may net income with the unusual loss removed be
     preferable to use for trend analysis?
d.   Speculate on why this loss is not considered extraordinary,
     or as a disposal of a segment.

SOLUTION:

a.   Lifeline Products
                Income Statement (Multiple-Step)
                For The Year Ended December 31, 2000

Sales		$3,000,000
Cost of sales		2,370,000
Gross profit		630,000
Selling and administrative expenses		322,000
Operating income		308,000
Other income:		
Rent income		14,000
Other expenses:		
Interest expense	$48,000	
Loss on sale of plant		
assets	16,000	(64,000)
Income before taxes		258,000
Income taxes		112,000
Net income		$ 146,000
Earnings per share		$7.30

b.   Tax rate:

Taxes		$ 112,000
Income before taxes		$ 258,000=43.4%
Loss on sale of plant assets		$ 16,000
Less: tax effects (43.4%)		(6,944)
Net item		9,056
Net income		146,000
Net income with unusual item removed		$ 155,056

c.   The loss from sale of plant assets may not be expected to
     recur; hence, future operations may be more closely related
     to net income with the loss removed.

d.   The item is not extraordinary because the sale of parts of
     plant assets is not unusual. The loss appears to relate to a
     few assets, not those of an entire segment. Treatment as a
     disposal of a segment is, therefore, unwarranted.

4.

Forta Company presents you with the following account balances
taken from the December 31, 2000 trial balance. Required:
Prepare a single-step income statement in proper form.

Sales	$200,000
Cost of Goods Sold	80,000
Cash	10,000
Selling Expenses	20,000
General and Administrative Expenses	15,000
Interest Income	3,000
Interest Expense	2,000
Accounts Receivable	15,000
Retained Earnings	60,000
Gain on Sale of Property	2,000
Accounts Payable	15,000
Accounts Receivable	20,000

Additional data:
1. 10,000 shares of common stock were outstanding the entire year.
2. The income tax rate is 35%.

SOLUTION:

Forta Company
Income Statement
For the Year Ended December 31, 2000

Sales	$200,000
Interest Income	3,000
Gain on Sale of Property	2,000
Total Revenue	$205,000
Costs and Expenses	
Cost of Goods Sold	80,000
Selling Expenses	20,000
General and Administrative Expenses	15,000
Interest Expense	2,000
Total Expense	$117,000
Income Before Income Taxes	88,000
Taxes on Income	30,800
Net Income	$ 57,200
Net Income Per Common Share	$ 5.72

5.

Patricia Company owns 25% of Sandra Company and accounts for the investment on the equity basis and does not consolidate. At the beginning of 2000, the investment in Sandra Company was $180,000. In 2000, Sandra Company earned $70,000 and paid dividends of $10,000.

Required:
a. How much will Patricia Company report as equity in earnings of Sandra Company in 2000?
b. How much cash flow will Patricia Company receive from Sandra Company in 2000?
c. Why does recognition of equity earnings cause problems in analysis?

SOLUTION:

a. $70,000 x 25% = $17,500
b. $10,000 x 25% = $2,500
c. Equity earnings cause a problem in analysis because the amount of earnings are usually different than the cash generated, as was illustrated in (a) and (b). Equity earnings also relate to profits of another company.

6.

Oregm Imports engages in the retail sale of household products and clothing. During 2000, the company disposed of the clothing segment. Oregm Imports had 150,000 shares of stock outstanding all year. The results of operations for 2000 follow.

	Household Products	Clothing
Net sales	$15,000,000	$3,900,000
Cost of goods sold	11,400,000	3,500,000
Operating expenses	1,400,000	300,000
Loss on disposal of clothing business (before income tax effect)		680,000
Interest expense	40,000	
Extraordinary loss from expropriation of operations in foreign country (before income tax effect)	80,000	

Income taxes of 40% apply to all items.

Required:
Prepare a multiple-step income statement for 2000 in good format.

SOLUTION:

Oregm Imports
Income Statement
For the Year 2000

Net sales			$15,000,000
Cost of goods sold			11,400,000
Gross profit			3,600,000
Operating expenses			1,400,000
Operating income			2,200,000
Interest expense			40,000
Income			2,160,000
Income tax (40%)			864,000
Income from continuing operations			1,296,000
Discontinued operations:			
Income during year	$100,000		
Less: taxes	(40,000)	$ 60,000	
Loss from disposal	$680,000		
Less: taxes	272,000	(408,000)	(348,000)
Income before extrarodinary loss			948,000
Extraordinary item:			
Loss from expropriation		$ 80,000	
Less: taxes		(32,000)	(48,000)
Net income			$ 900,000
Per common share:			
Income from continuing operations			$8.64
Discontinued operations			(2.32)
Income before extraordinary loss			6.32
Extraordinary item			(0.32)
Net income			$6.00

7.

Canco, Inc. owns 70% of Supersonics and consolidates this subsidiary. In 2000 Supersonics earned $100,000 after tax and Canco earned $1,000,000. Without consideration of minority interests, the stockholders' equity of Supersonics at the end of 2000 was $1,200,000.

Required:
a. Determine the minority share of earnings in 2000.
b. Determine the consolidated net income.
c. Determine the minority interest at the end of 2000 on the balance sheet.
d. How should minority interest be classified on the balance sheet for analysis?

SOLUTION:

a. Minority share: 30% x 100,000 = $30,000

b. Consolidated net income:

$1,000,000	Canco
+ 100,000	Supersonics
- 30,000	Minority Interest
$1,070,000	

c. Minority interest: 30% x $1,200,000 = $360,000.

d. Minority interest is best classified as a liability.

8.

Information for Scandinavian Products at the end of Year 4 follows:

Current Assets	$900,000
Current Liabilities	400,000
Fixed Assets, Net	600,000
Investments	100,000
Long-Term Debt	500,000
Dividends Declared on Common Stock During the Year	50,000
Income Summary (income)	225,000
Retained Earnings, January 1, Year 4	?
Common Stock	150,000
Premium on Common Stock	250,000

Required:
a. Find the ending balance in Retained Earnings as of December 31, Year 4.
b. Find the beginning balance in Retained Earnings as of January 1, Year 4.

SOLUTION:

a.   Ending Balance

Assets	Liabilities + Equity	
$ 900,000	$ 400,000	
600,000	500,000	
100,000	150,000	
	250,000	
$1,600,000	1,300,000	
	Retained Earnings Dec 31	300,000
	$1,600,000	

b. Retained Earnings, Dec. 31 = $300,000
    + Dividends   50,000
                                           350,000
    - Net Income (income summary)   225,000
    Retained Earnings, Jan. 1 $125,000

4-12

9.

Assume that Algary, Inc. uses the following financial statements:

 BS-Balance Sheet   IS-Income Statement   RE-Retained Earnings

Categories on these statements follow:
A. Current Assets   H. Sales and Other Operating Revenue
B. Investments   I. Cost of Goods Sold
C. Fixed Assets   J. Operating Expenses
D. Intangible Assets   K. Other Income
E. Current Liabilities   L. Other Expense
F. Long-Term Liabilities   M. Additions to Retained Earnings
G. Stockholders' Equity   N. Deductions from Retained Earnings

Required: Indicate by the statement abbreviation and category number how each of the following is best classified or where it is included in the computation. If an item is not reported anywhere, indicate by using the letter "X". Only the best answer should be selected.

For balance sheet accounts only, if the account balance is normally opposite that of a typical account (contra), set off the answer in parentheses, ( ).

Samples.   IS H   Sales
           (BS C)   Accumulated Depreciation

a. Capital Lease Obligations   m. Treasury Stock
      (due in 5 years and beyond)   n. Office Salaries Expense
b. Federal Income Taxes   o. Loss on Sale of Equipment
      Withheld   p. Bank Overdrafts
c. Accounts Payable   q. Unused Sales Supplies
d. Equipment   r. Bad Debt Expense
e. Unearned Management Fee   s. Petty Cash
      Revenue   t. Oil Wells (drilling
f. Unamortized Bond Discount   company)
      (due in 6 years)   u. Trade Name
g. Interest Expense   v. Stock Dividends Declared
h. Dividends Declared for   w. Gain from Winning
      the Period   Lawsuit. Suit was
i. Work In Process Inventory   filed in 1987
j. Purchase Returns and
      Allowances
k. Unexpired Office Insurance
      Expense
l. Rent Income (leasing company)

SOLUTION:

a. BS F
b. BS E
c. BS E
d. BS C
e. BS E
f. (BS F)
g. IS L
h. RE N
i. BS A
j. IS I
k. BS A
l. IS H
m. (BS G)
n. IS J
o. IS L
p. BS E
q. BS A
r. IS J
s. BS A
t. BS C
u. BS D
v. RE N
w. IS K

Chapter 5: BASICS OF ANALYSIS

MULTIPLE CHOICE

d   1.   Statements in which all items are expressed only in relative terms (percentages of a base) are termed:
    a. Vertical Statements
    b. Horizontal Statements
    c. Funds Statements
    d. Common-Size Statements
    e. none of these

c   2.   In financial statement analysis, ratios are:
    a. the only type of analysis where industry data are available
    b. absolute numbers converted to a common base
    c. fractions usually expressed in percent or times
    d. the only indication of the financial position of the firm
    e. none of the above

d   3.   Denver Dynamics has net income of $2,000,000. Oakland Enterprises has net income of $2,500,000. Which of the following best compares the profitability of Denver and Oakland?
    a. Oakland Enterprises is 25% more profitable than Denver Dynamics.
    b. Oakland Enterprises is more profitable than Denver Dynamics, but the comparison can't be quantified.
    c. Oakland Enterprises is only more profitable if it is smaller than Denver Dynamics.
    d. Further information is needed for a reasonable comparison.
        e. Oakland Enterprises is more profitable if it is a larger firm than Denver Dynamics.

d   4.   Which of the following can offer a type of comparison in financial statement analysis?
    a. past ratios and figures
    b. industry averages
    c. statistics of competitors
    d. all of the above
    e. none of the above

b   5.   Which of the following is **not** a source of industry statistics?
    a. Robert Morris Associates Annual Statement Studies
    b. The Wall Street Earnings Summary
    c. Value Line
    d. Standard and Poor's Industry Surveys
    e. The FTC Quarterly Report

c   6.   Robert Morris Associates Annual Statement Studies
          reported the following figures for manufacturers of
          screw machine products for the ratio of current assets
          to current debt. The following figures are for a
          particular industry's current ratio: 1.6; 1.3; 1.2.
          Which best describes these three numbers?
          a.   One third of each of the companies experienced each
               of the ratios.
          b.   The average ratio was 1.3. The best firm had 1.6;
               The worst had 1.2.
          c.   The median was 1.3. 1.6 is the figure for the upper
               quartile; 1.2 is the figure for the lower quartile.
          d.   The median was 1.3. 1.6 is the figure for the lower
               quartile; 1.2 is the figure for the upper quartile.
          e.   None of the above.

e   7.   A manufacturing firm will most likely have the heaviest
          investment in which type of assets?
          a.   cash
          b.   inventory
          c.   accounts receivable
          d.   investments
          e.   plant, property, and equipment

c   8.   A retailing firm has which type of inventory?
          a.   raw materials
          b.   work in process
          c.   merchandise
          d.   a and c
          e.   a,b, and c

e   9.   Which of the following would **not** be a user of financial
          statements?
          a.   management
          b.   bankers
          c.   employee unions
          d.   investment analysts
          e.   all of the above are users

d   10. Which of the following is a government document that
          provides industry statistics?
          a.   The Wall Street Journal
          b.   Business Week
          c.   Dun's
          d.   The DC Quarterly Financial Report
          e.   Standard and Poor's Industry Survey

d   11.   Suppose you are comparing two firms in the steel industry. One firm is large and the other is small. Which type of numbers would be most meaningful for statement analysis?
- a. Absolute numbers would be most meaningful for both the large and small firm.
- b. Absolute numbers would be most meaningful in the large firm; relative numbers would be most meaningful in the small firm.
- c. Relative numbers would be most meaningful for the large firm; absolute numbers would be most meaningful for the small firm.
- d. Relative numbers would be most meaningful for both the large and small firm, especially for interfirm comparisons.
- e. It is not meaningful to compare a large firm with a small firm.

c   12.   Various techniques are used in the analysis of financial data to emphasize the comparative and relative importance of the data presented and to evaluate the position of the firm. Which of the following is **not** one of the techniques used in analysis?
- a. ratio analysis
- b. common-size analysis
- c. theory consistency
- d. examination of relative size among firms
- e. review of descriptive material

d   13.   Liquidity ratios can be used:
- a. to measure the degree of protection of long-term suppliers of funds
- b. to measure borrowing capacity
- c. to measure the earning ability of a firm
- d. to measure the firm's ability to meet its current obligations
- e. to measure the worth of the firm

e   14.   Which of these statements is false?
- a. A ratio can be computed from any pair of numbers.
- b. Given the large quantity of variables included in financial statements, a very long list of meaningful ratios can be derived.
- c. Comparing ratios computed from income statement and balance sheet numbers can create difficulties due to the timing of the financial statements.
- d. Financial ratios are usually expressed in percent or times.
- e. In vertical analysis, a figure from the year's statement is compared with a base selected from the prior statement.

e   15. Which of these statements is **false**?
         a. Many companies will not clearly fit into any one
             industry.
         b. A financial service uses its best judgment as to
             which industry the firm best fits.
         c. The analysis of an entity's financial statements can
             be more meaningful if the results are compared with
             industry averages and with results of competitors.
         d. When using industry averages, it is often necessary
             to use an industry that the firm best fits.
         e. A company comparison should not be made with
             industry averages if the company does not clearly
             fit into any one industry.

b   16. Which of the following does **not** represent a problem with
         financial analysis?
         a. Financial statement analysis is an art; it requires
             judgment decisions on the part of the analyst.
         b. Financial analysis can be used to detect apparent
             liquidity problems.
         c. There are as many ratios for financial analysis as
             there are pairs of figures.
         d. Some industry ratio formulas vary from source to
             source.
         e. Adequate detailed disclosure of how the industry
             ratios are computed is often lacking.

d   17. Which of the following is a **false** statement as it
         relates to analysis?
         a. Profitability may not be a major consideration as
             long as the resources for repayment can be
             projected.
         b. Equity capital provides creditors with a cushion
             against loss.
         c. There is a difference between the objectives that
             are sought by short-term grantors of credit and
             those sought by long-term grantors of credit.
         d. If merchandise with a 20% markup is sold on credit,
             it would take ten successful sales of the same
             amount to make up for one sale not collected.
         e. The financial structure of the entity is of interest
             to creditors.

e   18. Management is a user of financial analysis. Which of
         the following comments does **not** represent a fair
         statement as to the management perspective?
         a. Management is interested in the view of investors.
         b. Management is interested in the view of creditors.
         c. Management is interested in the financial structure
             of the entity.
         d. Management is interested in the asset structure of
             the entity.
         e. Management is always interested in maximum
             profitability.

TRUE/FALSE

F   (1.) Liquidity ratios measure the degree of protection of long-term suppliers of funds.

F   2. A given ratio is always computed the same way, no matter what the source.

T   3. The ideal way to compare income statement figures, such as sales, to balance sheet figures, such as receivables, is to use a measure of the average for the balance sheet figures.

F   4. In vertical common-size analysis, the dollar figure for an account is expressed in terms of that same account figure for a selected base year.

F   5. Absolute figures usually have more meaning than ratio comparisons.

T   6. In order to determine the meaning of a ratio, some kind of comparison, such as an industry average or trend analysis, is helpful.

T   7. Different accounting methods can cause some ratios to differ substantially.

F   8. Dissimilar year ends will have no impact on the results of ratios.

F   9. The principal asset of a merchandising firm will usually be accounts receivable.

T   10. A service firm will usually have a low amount of inventory, consisting primarily of supplies.

T   11. The largest expense to a manufacturing firm is typically cost of goods sold.

F   12. The descriptive information in annual reports is not useful in statement analysis; only the financial statements themselves are of value.

T   13. The objectives of financial statement analysis by creditors will vary, based on the terms of the credit and the purpose.

T   14. Financial statement analysis is a judgmental process.

F   15. There is a standard list of ratios.

T   16. Common-size analysis involves expressing comparisons in percentages.

T   17.   Absolute figures or ratios are close to being
            meaningless unless compared to another figure.

T   18.   When performing year-to-year change analysis a
            meaningful percent change cannot be computed when one
            number is positive and the other number is negative.

PROBLEMS

1.

Comparative income statements for 2001 and 2000 follow.

	2001	2000
Sales	$9,434,000	$7,862,000
Cost of Sales	7,075,400	5,660,640
Gross Profit	2,358,600	2,201,360
Operating Expenses	1,367,690	1,365,060
Operating Income	990,910	836,300
Interest Expense	157,500	126,000
Earnings before Tax	833,410	710,300
Income Taxes	400,000	317,200
Net Income	$ 433,410	$ 393,100

Required:
a.   Prepare a vertical common-size analysis of this statement for
      each year, using sales as the base.
b.   Comment briefly on the changes between the two years, based
      on the vertical common-size statement.

SOLUTION:

a.

	2001	2000
Sales	100.0%	100.0%
Cost of Sales	75.0	72.0
Gross Profit	25.0	28.0
Operating Expenses	14.5	17.4
Operating Income	10.5	10.6
Interest Expense	1.7	1.6
Earnings Before Tax	8.8	9.0
Income Taxes	4.2	4.0
Net Income	4.6%	5.0%

b.   Cost of sales as a percent of sales have risen substantially.
      This increase is nearly offset by a decline in operating
      expense. Interest expense and taxes have both risen slightly
      in relation to sales.

2.

Toledo Toy, a manufacturer of infant's blocks, presented the following data in its last annual report. This trend analysis begins with the year of formation, 1998.

	2001	2000	1999	1998
Sales	$61,000	$41,000	$25,000	$13,000
Cost of Sales	$41,300	$28,175	$17,201	$ 9,000
Net Income	$ 9,919	$ 6,412	$ 3,850	$ 2,000
Cases of Blocks Shipped	33,126	22,681	13,900	7,400

Required:
a. Using 1998 as the base year, perform a horizontal common-size analysis.
b. Comment on the results of the horizontal analysis.

SOLUTION:

a.

	2001	2000	1999	1998
Sales	469.2	315.4	192.3	100.0%
Cost of Sales	458.9	313.1	191.1	100.0%
Net Income	496.0	320.6	192.5	100.0%
Cases of Blocks Shipped	447.6	306.5	187.8	100.0%

b.   Sales have risen rapidly. The cost of sales has risen more slowly than sales. Also, there has been a much faster rise in net income than in sales. The cases of blocks shipped has increased more slowly than sales dollars, indicating a rise in selling price or an improved mix of sales towards more expensive blocks.

3.

The following are simplified vertical common-size balance sheets for three firms—a retailer, a service firm, and a manufacturer.

Assets	Firm A	Firm B	Firm C
Cash	6.1%	8.1%	8.7%
Receivables	23.2	4.4	12.1
Inventory	31.1	1.5	24.5
Total Current Assets	60.4	14.0	45.3
Plant, Property and Equipment (net)	30.3	83.4	51.8
Investments	9.3	2.6	2.9
Total Assets	100.0%	100.0%	100.0%

Liabilities and Stockholders' Equity			
Total Current Liabilities	29.3%	11.5%	21.6%
Long-Term Debt	18.1	24.8	37.8
Total Stockholders' Equity	52.6	63.7	40.6
Total Liabilities and Stockholders' Equity	100.0%	100.0%	100.0%

Required: Match the statements to the type of firm and explain your choice.

SOLUTION:

Firm A is the retailing firm, due to the heavy investment in receivables and inventory with limited fixed assets. The store facilities may be rented.

Firm B is the service firm, due to the limited inventory.

Firm C is the manufacturing firm due to the combined heavy investment in inventory and also fixed assets. Also, it uses substantial long-term debt.

4.

a. Listed below are three groupings of financial ratios.
   Liquidity
   Long-term borrowing ability
   Profitability

Required:
Briefly describe what each one measures.

b. Groups of users of financial statements follow.

Required:
For each group, select the type of ratios from part (a) that each group might be most interested in. Briefly explain your choice.

        Suppliers of raw materials
        Potential stockholders
        Bondholders

SOLUTION:

a. Liquidity ratios measure the firm's ability to pay its current obligations.

    Long-term borrowing capacity measures the degree of protection of long-term suppliers of funds.

    Profitability ratios measure the earning ability of the firm.

b. Suppliers would be most interested in liquidity, since their goods and the related obligations are primarily short-term.

    Potential stockholders would be most interested in the earning ability of the firm since they share in residual profits.

    Bondholders would be most interested in the long-term borrowing capacity, since this measures the risk of default.

Chapter 6: LIQUIDITY OF SHORT-TERM ASSETS; RELATED DEBT-PAYING ABILITY

MULTIPLE CHOICE

e   1. Company A uses lifo and Company B uses fifo for inventory valuation. Otherwise, the firms are of similar size and have the same revenue and expense. Assume inflation. In analyzing liquidity and profitability of the two firms, which of the following will hold true?
   a. It is impossible to compare two firms with different inventory methods.
   b. Company B will have relatively higher profit and higher inventory turnover.
   c. Company B will have relatively lower profit and lower inventory turnover.
   d. Company A will have a higher current ratio and acid-test ratio, with the same profit.
   e. Company B will have relatively higher profit and a higher current ratio.

d   2. Which of the following would best indicate that the firm is carrying excess inventory?
   a. a decline in sales
   b. a decline in the current ratio
   c. a decline in days' sales in inventory
   d. stable current ratio with declining quick ratios
   e. a rise in total asset turnover

b   3. Which of the following types of businesses would normally have the shortest operating cycle?
   a. retail clothing store
   b. grocery store
   c. wholesale furniture store
   d. car manufacturer
   e. car dealer

c   4. Jones Company presents the following data for 2000:

   Receivables, less allowance for losses
     and discounts of $12,196 $ 266,700
   Net Sales $ 2,360,108
   Cost of Goods Sold $ 1,580,360

   The days' sales in receivables is
   a. 53.1
   b. 48.2
   c. 43.1
   d. 38.1
   e. none of the above

d   5.   Abbott Company presents the following data for 2000:

Receivables, end of year, less
     allowances for losses and discounts
     of $115,960 $ 2,370,100
Receivables, beginning of year, less
     allowance for losses and discounts
     of $102,330 $ 2,443,140
Net Sales $24,417,090

The accounts receivable turnover in times per year is:
a.   6.9
b.   7.9
c.   10.7
d.   9.7
e.   none of the above

c   6.   Smith Company presents the following data for 2000:

Inventories, beginning of year $ 310,150
Inventories, end of year $ 340,469
Cost of goods sold $2,103,696
Net Sales $8,690,150

The number of days' sales in inventory is:
a.   65.8
b.   60.8
c.   59.1
d.   58.1
e.   none of the above

a   7.   Shaffer Company presents the following data for 2000:

Net sales, 2000 $3,007,124
Net sales, 1999 $2,193,247
Cost of goods sold, 2000 $2,000,326
Cost of goods sold, 1999 $1,000,120
Inventory, beginning of 2000 $ 341,169
Inventory, end of 2000 $ 376,526

The merchandise inventory turnover for 2000 is:
a. 5.6
b. 15.6
c. 7.5
d. 7.7
e. none of the above

c   8.   Szabo Company computed the following data for 2000:

Days' sales in receivables   38.7 days
Accounts receivable turnover   9.6 times
Accounts receivable turnover in days   35.1 days
Days' sales in inventory   68.5 days
Merchandise inventory turnover   5.9 times
Inventory turnover in days   58.7 days

The estimated operating cycle for 2000 is:
a.   97.4 days
b.   107.2 days
c.   93.8 days
d.   108.0 days
e.   none of the above

b   9.   Typically which of the following would be considered to
be the most indicative of a firm's short-term debt
paying ability?
a.   working capital
b.   current ratio
c.   acid-test ratio
d.   cash ratio
e.   days' sales in receivables

d   10. If a firm has pledged its receivables and its inventory,
then the best indicator of its short-term liquidity may
be indicated by:
a.   working capital
b.   current ratio
c.   acid-test ratio
d.   cash ratio
e.   days' sales in receivables

e   11. Which of the following would **not** be classified as a
current asset?
a.   cash
b.   marketable securities
c.   receivables
d.   inventories
e.   investments

a   12. Which of the following types of business would normally
have the longest operating cycle?
a.   seller of resort property
b.   car dealer
c.   car manufacturer
d.   grocery store
e.   record store

a   13.   Which of the following accounts would **not** be classified as a current asset?
   a. cash restricted for retirement of bonds
   b. cash and equivalents
   c. cash and certificates of deposit
   d. time deposits
   e. cash

a   14.   Unrealized losses for long-term investments should usually be reported in the:
   a. stockholders' equity section of the balance sheet
   b. income statement
   c. current assets section of the balance sheet
   d. current liabilities section of the balance sheet
   e. long-term liabilities section of the balance sheet

e   15.   Which of the following does **not** bear on the quality of receivables?
   a. shortening the credit terms
   b. lengthening the credit terms
   c. right of return privilege
   d. lengthening the outstanding period
   e. all of the above (a-d) bear on the quality of receivables

e   16.   Which of the following reasons should **not** be considered in order to explain why the receivables appear to be abnormally high:
   a. Sales volume expanded materially late in the year.
   b. Receivables have collectibility problems and possibly some should have been written off.
   c. The company seasonally dates invoices.
   d. Material amount of receivables are on the installment basis.
   e. Sales volume decreases materially late in the year.

e   17.   Which of the following is **not** an acceptable inventory costing method?
   a. specific identification
   b. last-in, first-out (lifo)
   c. first-in, first-out (fifo)
   d. average cost
   e. next-in, first-out (nifo)

d   18.   Which of the following would **not** be a reasonable
          conclusion when comparing lifo - fifo under an
          inflationary condition?
          a.   Lifo generally results in a lower profit than does
               fifo.
          b.   Fifo reports a higher inventory ending balance.
          c.   Lifo results in a lower profit figure than does
               fifo.
          d.   Lifo would probably be used for inventory that has a
               high turnover rate because there would be an
               immaterial difference in the results between lifo
               and fifo.
          e.   The cash flow under lifo is greater than the cash
               flow under fifo by the difference in the resulting
               tax between the two methods.

a   19.   Which of the following current assets will **not** generate
          cash in the future?
          a.   prepayments
          b.   accounts receivable
          c.   inventory
          d.   marketable securities
          e.   notes receivable

e   20.   Which of the following ratios does **not** represent some
          form of comparison between accounts in current assets
          and accounts in current liabilities?
          a.   working capital
          b.   current ratio
          c.   acid-test ratio
          d.   cash ratio
          e.   merchandise inventory turnover

b   21.   Which of the following ratios would generally be used to
          evaluate a firm's overall liquidity position?
          a.   working capital
          b.   current ratio
          c.   acid-test ratio
          d.   cash ratio
          e.   inventory turnover in days

TRUE/FALSE

F   1.   Compensating balances reduce the amount of cash
         available to the borrower to meet obligations and they
         decrease the effective interest rate for the borrower.

T   2.   To qualify as a marketable security, the investment must
         be readily marketable and it must be the intent of
         management to convert the investment to cash within the
         current operating cycle or a year, whichever is longer.

F 3. In terms of liquidity, it is to management's advantage to show investments under investments instead of marketable securities.

T 4. By reporting marketable equity securities under current assets, management picks up a liquidity advantage.

T 5. The valuation problem from waiting to collect a receivable is ignored in the valuation of receivables and notes that are classified in current assets.

T 6. Under the allowance method, the charge off of a specific account receivable does not influence the income statement nor the net receivable on the balance sheet at the time of the charge off.

T 7. Using the direct write-off method, the bad debt expense is recorded as a specific customer's account is determined to be noncollectible.

F 8. The direct write-off method frequently results in the bad debt expense being recognized in the year subsequent to the sale, and thus results in a proper matching of expense with revenue.

T 9. When a company has receivables that are due beyond one year or accounting cycle from the balance sheet date, and when it is the industry practice to include these receivables in current assets, they will be included in current assets even though they do not technically meet the guidelines to qualify as current assets.

F 10. The receivables of a company with installment receivables would normally be considered to be of higher quality than the receivables of a company that did not have installment receivables.

T 11. If days' sales in receivables are materially longer than the credit terms, this indicates a collection problem.

T 12. The days' sales in receivables ratio gives an indication of the length of time that the receivables have been outstanding at the end of the year. This indication can be misleading if sales are seasonal and/or the company uses a natural business year.

T 13. Days' sales in receivables may be abnormally high at the end of the year if sales volume expanded materially late in the year.

F 14. Days' sales in receivables may be abnormally high if a material amount of sales are on a cash basis.

T   15.   When doing external analysis, many of the reasons why the days' sales in receivables is abnormally high or low cannot be determined without access to internal information.

F   16.   Inventory is particularly sensitive to changes in business activity. Therefore, management should keep inventory at a minimum.

T   17.   Because the cost of specific inventory items is not usually practical to determine, it is necessary for management to select a cost flow assumption.

T   18.   A firm that has been on lifo for many years may have some inventory costs that go back ten years or more.

F   19.   Under inflationary conditions, fifo generally results in a lower profit than does lifo and this difference can be substantial.

T   20.   A low sales to working capital ratio tentatively indicates an unprofitable use of working capital.

T   21.   Working capital of a business is the excess of current assets over current liabilities.

F   22.   The lifo inventory costing method usually results in working capital being overstated.

F   23.   The lifo inventory costing method results in the acid-test ratio being overstated.

F   24.   The cash ratio is usually a good indication of the liquidity of the firm.

F   25.   Management should usually strive to keep the cash ratio high.

T   26.   The ability of an entity to maintain its short-term debt-paying ability is important to all users of financial statements.

T   27.   Even an entity on a very profitable course will find itself bankrupt if it fails to meets its obligations to short-term creditors.

F   28.   Current assets are assets that (1) are in the form of cash, (2) will be realized in cash, or (3) conserve the use of cash within the operating cycle of a business or for one year, whichever is shorter.

T   29.   The operating cycle is the time between the acquisition of inventory and the realization of cash from selling the inventory.

F 30. In order to classify cash as a current asset, it must be free from any restrictions that would prevent its deposit or use to pay creditors classified as long-term.

T 31. The use of the allowance for doubtful accounts results in the bad debt expense being charged to the period of sale.

T 32. Customer concentration can be an important consideration in the quality of receivables.

F 33. A shortening of the credit terms is an indication that there will be more risk in the collection of future receivables.

T 34. The company with the natural business year tends to overstate its accounts receivable turnover, thus overstating its liquidity.

T 35. The election to use lifo for taxes governs the firm's financial reporting.

F 36. If the company closes the year when the activities are at a peak, the number of days' sales in inventory would tend to be overstated and the liquidity would be overstated.

T 37. An approximation of the operating cycle can be determined from the receivable liquidity figures and the inventory liquidity figures.

F 38. Working capital is considered to be more indicative of the short-term debt-paying ability than is the current ratio.

T 39. Liquidity problems with receivables and/or inventory means that the current ratio needs to be much higher than when there are no such liquidity problems.

T 40. Significant weight is seldom given to the cash ratio unless the firm is in financial trouble.

PROBLEMS

1.

Required:
Determine the cost of goods sold of a firm with the financial data given below:

```
            Current Ratio   2.4 to 1
             *Acid-Test Ratio                    2.1 to 1
              Current Liabilities               $ 400,000
              Inventory Turnover
              (using ending inventory)            4 times
```

*Assume that the acid-test ratio is computed as follows

Current Assets - Inventory
Current Liabilities

SOLUTION:

$$\text{Current Ratio} = \frac{\text{Current Assets}}{\text{Current Liabilities}} = \frac{X}{\$400,000} = 2.4$$

$$\text{Current Assets} = (\$400,000)(2.4) = \$960,000$$

$$\text{Acid-Test Ratio} = \frac{\text{Current Assets - Inventory}}{\text{Current Liabilities}} = \frac{\$960,000-X}{\$400,000} = 2.1$$

$$\$960,000 - X = \$840,000$$
$$= \$120,000$$

$$\text{Inventory Turnover} = \frac{\text{Cost of Sales}}{\text{Inventory}} = \frac{X}{\$120,000} = 4$$

$$\text{Cost of Sales} = \$480,000$$

2.

Each of the following would generally be thought of as a favorable indicator of the firm's financial position.

a. A current ratio well above 2.0, which is substantially higher than that for other firms in the industry.

b. Collection period significantly lower than for several recent periods.

c. Rapidly rising merchandise inventory turnover.

Required:
In each case, give an example of circumstances underlying the ratio that might represent an unfavorable development.

SOLUTION:

a. A high current ratio can mean overstocked inventory or doubtful receivables. Either of these accounts being high could cause the current ratio to be misleading.

b. The firm may have substantially tightened its credit policy. This might have resulted in a major loss of customers.

c. Rapidly rising turnover might mean that production is
    unable to generate goods as quickly as possible and that
    the firm is running a risk of stockouts.

3.

Required:
How will switching from fifo to lifo for inventory valuation
affect financial analysis of liquidity and profitability? Cite
two ratios that will be affected and indicate how they will
change. (Assume an inflationary condition.)

SOLUTION:
Lifo inventory valuation results in higher cost of sales and
lower inventory valuation.

It will cause lower profitability and tax outflow. Merchandise
inventory turnover will appear much higher, since the cost of
sales will be higher and average inventory much lower. Days'
sales in inventory will be lower, since the cost of sales will
be higher, giving higher daily cost of sales to divide into
lower inventory. The liquidity position will be reduced in
terms of working capital and the current ratio.

4.

Decort Company's working capital accounts at December 31, 2000,
are given below:

Current Assets:		
Cash		$100,000
Marketable Securities		50,000
Accounts Receivable	$250,000	
Less Allowance for		
Doubtful Accounts	(20,000)	230,000
Inventory, Lifo		300,000
Prepaid		8,000
Total Current Assets		$688,000
Current Liabilities:		
Accounts Payable		$200,000
Notes Payable		50,000
Taxes Payable		10,000
Accrued Liabilities		30,000
Total Current Liabilities		$290,000

During 2001, DeCort Company completed the following
transactions:
a. Purchased fixed assets for cash, $20,000.
b. Exchanged DeCort Company common stock for land.
    Estimated value of transaction, $80,000.
c. Payment of $40,000 on short-term notes payable.
d. Sold marketable securities costing $20,000 for
    $25,000 cash.

e. Sold DeCort Company common stock for $70,000.
f. Wrote off an account receivable in the amount of
    $20,000.
g. Declared a cash dividend in the amount of $5,000.
h. Paid the above cash dividend.
i. Sold inventory costing $10,000 for $15,000 cash.
j. Sold inventory costing $5,000 for $8,000, on account.
k. Paid accounts payable in the amount of $20,000.
l. Sold marketable securities costing $20,000 for
    $20,000 cash.
m. Issued a credit memo on an account receivable,
    $1,000.

Required:
a. Compute the following as of December 31, 2000:
    1) working capital
    2) current ratio
    3) acid-test ratio (conservative)
    4) cash ratio
    (These ratios are to be computed using only the December
    31, 2000 data.)
b. For 2001, indicate the effect of each of the transactions
    given on working capital, current ratio, acid-test ratio,
    and cash ratio. Give the effect in terms of +,-, or none.
    Consider each transaction to be the first transaction of
    the year. Assume at the start of the year that the current
    ratio is over 2 to 1, the acid-test ratio is over 1 to 1,
    and the cash ratio is less than 1 to 1.

Format:

	The Effect On			
	Working	Current	Acid-Test	Cash
Transaction	Capital	Ratio	Ratio	Ratio

SOLUTION:
a. 1) Working Capital = Current Assets - Current Liabilities

            = $688,000 - $290,000
            = $398,000

    2) Current Ratio = $\dfrac{\text{Current Assets}}{\text{Current Liabilities}}$

            = $\dfrac{\$688,000}{\$290,000}$ = 2.37

    3) Acid-Test Ratio = $\dfrac{\text{Cash Equivalents + Marketable Securities + Net Receivables}}{\text{Current Liabilities}}$

            = $\dfrac{\$100,000 + \$50,000 + \$230,000}{\$290,000}$ = 1.31

6-11

4) Cash Ratio = $\dfrac{\text{Cash Equivalents} + \text{Marketable Securities}}{\text{Current Liabilities}}$

$$= \dfrac{\$ 100,000 + \$ 50,000}{\$290,000} = 0.52$$

b.

		The Effect On		
Transaction	Working Capital	Current Ratio	Acid-Test Ratio	Cash Ratio
a.	-	-	-	-
b.	none	none	none	none
c.	none	+	+	-
d.	+	+	+	+
e.	+	+	+	+
f.	none	none	none	none
g.	-	-	-	-
h.	none	+	+	-
i	+	+	+	+
j	+	+	+	
none				
k	none	+	+	-
l	none	none	none	none
m	-	-	-	none

5.

Bill's Produce does 60 percent of its business during June, July, and August.

	For Year Ended December 31, 2001	For Year Ended July 31, 2001
Net Sales	$700,000	$690,000
Receivables, less allowance for doubtful accounts:		
Beginning of period (allowance, January 1 $2,000; August 1, $3,000)	$ 45,000	$ 80,000
End of period (allowance, December 31 $3,000; July 31, $3,500)	$ 50,000	$ 85,000

Required:
a.   Compute the days' sales in receivables for July 31, 2001 and December 31, 2001, based on the data above.
b.   Compute the accounts receivable turnover for the period ended July 31, 2001 and December 31, 2001.
c.   Comment on the results from (a) and (b).

SOLUTION:
a.   Days' sales in receivables   12/31/01   7/31/01

     Gross Receivables $ 53,000 $ 88,500
     Net Sales / 365 $ 700,000 $ 690,000
                                          365   365

                                       =   27.6   = 46.8

                                       _____Net Sales_____
b.   Accounts Receivable   = Average Gross Receivables

     12/31/01: $\dfrac{\$700,000}{\$47,000 \, + \, \$53,000) \, / \, 2} = 14.0$

     7/31/01: $\dfrac{\$690,000}{\$83,000 \, + \, \$88,500) \, / \, 2} = 8.0$

c.   Bill's Produce is a seasonal business. Therefore, the
     computation of days' sales in receivables and accounts
     receivable turnover are not realistic. These figures would
     be helpful when comparing with prior years on the same
     date.

6.
Required:
a.   Stark Company has computed its accounts receivable turnover
     in days to be 36. Compute the accounts receivable turnover
     per year.

b.   Stark Company has computed its accounts receivable turnover
     per year to be 10. Compute the accounts receivable
     turnover in days.

c.   Stark Company has gross receivables at the end of the year
     of $380,000 and net sales for the year of $1,850,000.
     Compute the days' sales in receivables at the end of the
     year.

d.   Stark Company has net sales of $2,500,000 and average gross
     receivables of $224,000. Compute the accounts receivable
     turnover.

SOLUTION:

a. $\dfrac{Accounts\ Receivable}{Turnover} = \dfrac{365}{Receivable\ Turnover\ in\ Days} = \dfrac{365}{36} = \dfrac{10.1}{Times}$

b. $\dfrac{Accounts\ Receivable}{Turnover\ in\ Days} = \dfrac{365}{Accounts\ Receivable\ Turnover\ per\ Year} = \dfrac{365}{10} = \dfrac{36.5}{days}$

c. Days' Sales in   = Gross Receivables   = $380,000
    Receivables   Net Sales/365 $1,850,000/365

                          = 75.0 days

d. Accounts Receivable   =   Sales   = $2,500,000
                             Average Gross $224,000
                             Receivables

                          = 11.2 times

7.

Alpha Company would like to estimate how long it will take to
realize cash from its ending inventory. For this purpose the
following data are submitted:

Accounts Receivable, less allowance for doubtful accounts of $40,000	$ 660,000
Ending Inventory	$ 750,000
Net Sales	$5,650,000
Cost of Goods Sold	$4,250,000

Days' Sales in Inventory   = Ending Inventory
                                Cost of Goods Sold/365

Days' Sales in Receivables   = Gross Receivables
                                Net Sales/365

Required:
Estimate how long it will take to realize cash from the ending
inventory.

SOLUTION:

$\dfrac{\$~750,000}{\$4,250,000/365} = 64.4 \qquad \dfrac{\$~700,000}{\$5,650,000/365} = 45.2$

64.4 + 45.2 = 109.6 days

8.

Hind Company presents the following data for 2000:

Accounts Receivable, less allowance for doubtful accounts of $40,000	$ 780,000
Ending Inventory, lifo (estimated replacement cost $800,000)	$ 500,000

Net Sales	$4,750,000
Cost of Goods Sold (estimated replacement cost, $4,150,000)	$3,550,000

Required:
a. Compute the days' sales in receivables.
b. Compute the days' sales in inventory, using the cost figure.
c. Compute the days' sales in inventory, using the replacement cost for the inventory and the cost of goods sold.
d. Explain which days' sales in inventory figure is probably more realistic, the one computed in (b) or (c).

SOLUTION:
a. Days' Sales in Receivables $= \dfrac{\text{Gross Receivables}}{\text{Net Sales}/365}$

$$= \frac{\$820,000}{\$4,750,000/365} = 63.0$$

b. Days' Sales in Inventory $= \dfrac{\text{Inventory}}{\text{Cost of Goods Sold}/365}$

$$= \frac{\$500,000}{\$3,550,000/365} = 51.4$$

c. Days' Sales in Inventory (using the replacement cost) $= \dfrac{\text{Inventory}}{\text{Estimated Goods sold}}$

$$= \frac{\$800,000}{\$4,150,000/365} = 70.36$$

d. The days' sales in inventory figure computed in (c) is probably more realistic because it compares similar costs for both inventory and cost of goods sold.

9.

Required:
Comment on the usual influence from a switch to lifo from fifo on the following variables during an inflationary period:

    a.   revenue
    b.   gross profit
    c.   cost of goods sold
    d.   profit
    e.   income taxes
    f.   cash flow

SOLUTION:
a. A switch to lifo will usually not influence revenue because revenue is usually more demand/supply-related than cost-related.

b. Gross profit will usually decline because of higher cost of goods sold.

c. Cost of goods sold will increase because of using the most recent cost.

d. Profits will decrease because of the higher cost of goods sold.

e. Income taxes will decrease because of the lower profit.

f. Cash flow will increase because of the lower taxes.

10.

Anne Elizabeth Company's Balance Sheet for December 31, 2000, and Income Statement for the year ended December 31, 2000, are given below:

Balance Sheet
Anne Elizabeth Company
December 31, 2000

	2000	1999
Assets:		
Current Assets:		
Cash	$ 50,450	$ 28,538
Marketable Securities	25,000	20,500
Accounts Receivable, less allowance		
of $10,000	60,000	50,000
Inventory, Lifo	90,000	70,000
Prepaid	8,000	7,000
Total Current Assets	233,450	176,038
Property, Plant, and Equipment:		
Land	9,000	8,000
Buildings and Equipment	220,000	210,000
	229,000	218,000
Less accumulated depreciation	(68,000)	(60,000)
Total Assets	$394,450	$334,038
Liabilities and Shareholders' Equity:		
Current Liabilities:		
Accounts Payable	$ 35,000	$ 30,000
Accrued Compensation	8,000	7,000
Income Taxes	7,000	6,000
Total Current Liabilities	50,000	43,000
Long-Term Debt	40,000	11,038
Shareholders' Equity:		
Common Shares	60,000	60,000
Retained Earnings	244,450	220,000
	304,450	280,000
Total Liabilities and Shareholders' Equity	$394,450	$334,038

Income Statement
Anne Elizabeth Company
For the Year Ended December 31, 2000

	2000	1999	1998
Net sales	$718,500	$650,500	$640,000
Cost of goods sold	580,000	520,000	515,000
Gross profit	138,500	130,500	125,000
Operating expenses:			
Selling, general, and			
administrative	71,000	67,000	65,000
Interest	4,000	3,000	2,500
	75,000	70,000	67,500
Earnings before income taxes	63,500	60,500	57,500
Income taxes	30,000	29,000	28,000
Net earnings	$ 33,500	$ 31,500	$ 29,500

Required:
a. Compute the following ratios for 2000:
    1. Accounts receivable turnover
    2. Merchandise inventory turnover
    3. Working capital
    4. Current ratio
    5. Acid-test ratio (conservative)
    6. Sales to working capital

SOLUTION:
1.

$$\text{Accounts receivable turnover} = \frac{\text{Net Sales}}{\text{Average Gross Receivables}}$$

$$\frac{\$718,500}{[(\$60,000 + \$10,000) + (\$50,000 + \$10,000)]/2} = \frac{\$718,500}{\$65,000} = 11.05$$

2. $$\text{Merchandise Inventory Turnover} = \frac{\$580,000}{\$80,000} = 7.25$$

$$\frac{\$580,000}{(\$90,000 + \$70,000)/2} = \frac{\$580,000}{\$80,000} = 7.25$$

3. Working capital = Current Assets - Current Liabilities

$233,450 - $50,000 = $183,450

6-17

4. Current ratio = Current assets/Current liabilities

$$\frac{\$233,450}{\$50,000} = 4.67$$

5. $\text{Acid - test Ratio} = \dfrac{\text{Cash Equivalents + Marketable Securities + Net Receivables}}{\text{Current Liabilities}}$

$$\frac{\$50,450 + \$25,000 + \$60,000}{\$50,000} = \frac{\$135,450}{\$50,000} = 2.71$$

6. $\text{Sales to Working Capital} = \dfrac{\text{Sales}}{\text{Average Working Capital}}$

$$\frac{\$718,500}{[(\$233,450 - \$50,000) + (\$176,038 - \$43,000)]/2} = \frac{\$718,500}{\$158,244} = 4.54$$

Chapter 7: LONG-TERM DEBT-PAYING ABILITY

MULTIPLE CHOICE

e 1. Jones Company has long-term debt of $1,000,000 while
       Smith Company, Jones' competitor, has long-term debt of
       $200,000. Which of the following statements best
       represents an analysis of the long-term debt position of
       these two firms?
       a. Smith Company's times interest earned should be
           lower than Jones.
       b. Jones obviously has too much debt when compared to
           its competitor.
       c. Jones should sell more stock and use less debt.
           d.   Smith has 5 times better long-term borrowing
           ability than Jones.
       e. None of the above.

c 2. Ingram Dog Kennels had the following financial
       statistics for 2000:

       Long-term debt $400,000
            (average rate of interest is 8%)
       Interest expense   35,000
       Net income   48,000
       Income tax   46,000
       Operating income   107,000

       What is the times interest earned for 2000?
       a. 11.4 times
       b.   3.3 times
       c.   3.1 times
       d.   3.7 times
       e. none of the above

b 3. A times interest earned ratio of .90 to 1 means:
       a. that the firm will default on its interest payment
       b. that net income is less than the interest expense
       c. that the cash flow is less than the net income
       d. that the cash flow exceeds the net income
       e. none of the above

c 4. Which of the following will **not** cause times interest
       earned to drop? Assume no other changes than those
       listed.
       a. an increase in bonds payable with no change in
           operating income
       b. an increase in interest rates
       c. a rise in preferred stock dividends
       d. a rise in cost of goods sold with no change in
           interest expense
       e. a drop in sales with no change in interest expense

e   5. A times interest earned ratio indicates that:
        a. preferred stock has no maturity date
        b. the debt will never become due
        c. the firm will be able to repay the principal when
            due
        d. the principal can be refinanced
        e. none of the above

b   6. Jordan Manufacturing reports the following capital
        structure:

        Current liabilities $100,000
        Long-term debt   400,000
        Deferred income taxes   10,000
        Preferred stock   80,000
        Common stock   100,000
        Premium on common stock   180,000
        Retained earnings   170,000

        What is the debt ratio?
        a. .48
        b. .49
        c. .93
        d. .96
        e. none of the above

d   7. The debt ratio indicates:
        a. the ability of the firm to pay its current
            obligations
        b. the efficiency of the use of total assets
        c. the magnification of earnings caused by leverage
        d. a comparison of liabilities with total assets
        e. none of the above

a   8. Joseph and John, Inc., had the following balance sheet
        results for 2000:
                                                 (in millions)
        Current liabilities $12.6
        Bonds payable   18.6
        Lease obligations   2.7
        Minority interest   1.4
        Common stock   8.6
        Retained earnings   22.9
                                                     $66.8

        Compute the debt-equity ratio.
        a. 112.1%
        b.   87.6%
        c.   67.6%
        d.   46.7%
        e. none of the above

d   9. Which of the following statements best compares long-term borrowing capacity ratios?
 a. The debt/equity ratio is more conservative than the debt ratio.
 b. The debt ratio is more conservative than the debt/equity ratio.
 c. The debt/equity ratio is more conservative than the debt to tangible net worth ratio.
 d. The debt to tangible net worth ratio is more conservative than the debt/equity ratio.
 e. The debt ratio is more conservative than the debt to tangible net worth ratio.

d   10. In computing debt to tangible net worth, which of the following is **not** subtracted in the denominator?
 a. copyrights
 b. goodwill
 c. patents
 d. investments
 e. trademarks

b   11. A fixed charge coverage:
 a. is a balance sheet indication of debt carrying ability
 b. is an income statement indication of debt carrying ability
 c. is a liquidity ratio
 d. frequently includes research and development
 e. computation is standard from firm to firm

c   12. The following financial statement data are taken from Xeron Company's 2000 annual report:

	(in millions)
Current assets	$12.6
Investments	9.4
Intangibles	6.8
Tangible assets (net)	58.1
Current liabilities	6.4
Long-term debt	39.7
Stockholders' equity	40.8

Compute the debt ratio.
 a. 196.9%
 b. 113.0%
 c. 53.0%
 d. 45.7%
 e. none of the above

b   13.   The following financial statement data are taken from Xeron Company's 2000 annual report: Compute the debt to tangible net worth ratio.

	(in millions)
Current assets	$12.6
Investments	9.4
Intangibles	6.8
Tangible assets (net)	58.1
Current liabilities	6.4
Long-term debt	39.7
Stockholders' equity	40.8

    a.   146.8%
    b.   135.6%
    c.   53.0%
    d.   45.7%
    e.   none of the above

c   14.   If a firm has substantial capital or financing leases disclosed in the footnotes but not capitalized in the financial statements, then:
    a.   the times interest earned ratio will be overstated, based upon the financial statements
    b.   the fixed charge ratio will be overstated, based upon the financial statements
    c.   the debt ratio will be understated
    d.   the working capital will be understated
    e.   none of the above

b   15.   Under the Employee Retirement Income Security Act, a company can be liable for its pension plan up to:
    a.   30 percent of its total assets
    b.   30 percent of its net worth
    c.   40 percent of its total assets
    d.   40 percent of its net worth
    e.   50 percent of its total assets

e   16.   Included in the Employee Retirement Income Security Act are the following:
    a.   provisions requiring minimum funding of pension plans
    b.   minimum rights to employees upon termination of their employment
    c.   creation of the Pension Benefit Guaranty Corporation
    d.   a and b
    e.   a,b, and c

e   17.   What significant improvement in the financial reporting of pensions have pension accounting rules provided?
   a. determination of the expense for the income statement
   b. limited balance sheet recognition of pension liabilities
   c. improved disclosure
   d. a and b
   e. a,b, and c

e   18.   There are a number of assumptions about future events that must be made regarding a defined benefit plan. An assumption that does **not** need to be made is:
   a. interest rates
   b. employee turnover
   c. mortality rates
   d. compensation
   e. how long the firm will continue

d   19.   Which of the following statements is **not** correct?
   a. A ratio that indicates a firm's long-term debt-paying ability from the income statement view is the times interest earned.
   b. Some of the items on the income statement that are excluded in order to compute times interest earned are interest expense, income taxes, and unusual or infrequent items.
   c. Capitalized interest should be included with interest expense when computing times interest earned.
   d. Usually the highest times interest coverage in the most recent five year period is used as the primary indication of the interest coverage.
   e. In the short run, a firm can often meet its interest obligations, even when the times interest earned is less than 1.00.

a   20.   Which of these items represents a definite commitment to pay out funds in the future?
   a. bonds payable
   b. reserves for rebuilding furnaces
   c. deferred taxes
   d. minority shareholders' interests
   e. redeemable preferred stock

e 21. Which of the following statements is **not** true relating
       to a capitalized (capital) lease?
       a. A capital lease is handled as if the lessee bought
          the asset.
       b. The leased asset is in the fixed assets and the
          related obligation is included in liabilities.
       c. On the balance sheet, the capitalized asset amount
          will **not** usually agree with the capitalized
          liability amount because the liability is reduced by
          payments, and the asset is reduced by depreciation
          taken.
       d. Usually, a company depreciates capitalized leases
          faster than payments are made.
       e. On the balance sheet, the capitalized asset amount
          will usually be higher than the capitalized
          liability amount.

e 22. Which of the following statements is **not** true relating
       to a defined contribution pension plan?
       a. A defined contribution plan defines the
          contributions of the company to the pension plan.
       b. Once the defined contribution is paid, the company
          has no further obligation to the pension plan.
       c. This type of plan shifts the risk to the employee as
          to whether the pension plan will grow to provide for
          a reasonable pension payment upon retirement.
       d. There is no problem estimating the company's pension
          expense.
       e. This type of plan presents substantial problems in
          estimating the pension liability.

b 23. A number of assumptions about future events must be made
       regarding a defined benefit plan. Which of the
       following does **not** represent one of the assumptions?
       a. interest rates
       b. termination date for the firm
       c. employee turnover
       d. mortality rates
       e. compensation

TRUE/FALSE

F 1. When analyzing a firm's long-term debt-paying ability,
      we only want to determine the firm's ability to pay the
      principal.

T 2. In general, the profitability of a firm is <u>not</u>
      considered to be important in determining the short-term
      debt-paying ability of the firm.

T 3. A good times interest earned record would be indicated
      by a relatively high, stable coverage for the times
      interest earned coverage.

T   4. Minority shareholders' interest in earnings of
         subsidiaries are included in earnings for the times
         interest earned coverage.

T   5. Equity earnings are excluded from earnings for the times
         interest earned coverage.

F   6. Capitalized interest should not be considered as part of
         interest in the times interest earned computation.

F   7. To get a better indication of a firm's ability to cover
         interest payments in the long run, the non-cash charges
         for depreciation, depletion, and amortization can be
         added back to the times interest earned ratio.

T   8. When a portion of operating lease payments is included
         in fixed charges, it is an effort to recognize the true
         total interest that the firm is paying.

T   9. Under generally accepted accounting principles, an item
         must clearly represent a commitment to pay out funds in
         the future in order to be classified as a liability.

T   10. When a firm is expensing an item faster on the tax
         return than on the financial statements, a deferred tax
         liability is the result.

T   11. As with the debt ratio and the debt/equity ratio, from a
         long-term debt-paying ability view, the lower the debt
         to tangible net worth ratio the better.

T   12. The debt to tangible net worth ratio is a more
         conservative ratio than the debt ratio.

T   13. A joint venture can add significant potential
         liabilities to the parent company that are not on the
         face of the balance sheet.

T   14. A potential significant liability is possible if the
         company withdraws from a multiemployer pension plan.

F   15. A defined benefit plan shifts the risk to the employee
         as to whether the pension funds will grow to provide for
         a reasonable pension payment upon retirement.

T   16. If an employee is in the pension plan, rights under this
         plan will be lost if the employee leaves the firm prior
         to receiving a vested interest.

F   17. The balance sheet pension liability considers the
         projected benefit obligation.

T   18.   The higher the interest rate used, the lower the present value of the pension liability, and the lower the immediate pension cost.

T   19.   Some companies achieve benefits by hundreds of millions of dollars by a pension termination.

F   20.   Times interest earned indicates a firm's long-term debt-paying ability from the balance sheet view.

T   21.   Capitalization of interest results in interest being added to a fixed asset instead of expensed.

T   22.   In the short run, a firm can often meet its interest obligations even when the times interest earned is less than 1.00.

F   23.   The tax expense for the financial statements often agrees with the taxes payable.

T   24.   Some revenue and expense items never go on the tax return, but do go on the income statement.

PROBLEMS

1.

Laura Bella Company reports the following statement of income:

Operating Revenues	$4,800
Costs and Expenses:	
Cost of Sales	(2,000)
Selling, Service, Administrative, and General Expense	(1,500)
Income Before Interest Expense and Income Taxes	1,300
Interest Expense	(180)
Income Before Income Taxes	1,120
Income Taxes	(350)
Net Income	$ 770

Note: Depreciation expense totals $300; preferred dividends total $60; operating lease payments total $180. Assume that 1/3 of operating lease payments is for interest.

Required:
a.   Compute the times interest earned.
b.   Compute the fixed charge coverage.

SOLUTION:

a.

$$\text{Times Interest Earned} = \frac{\text{Recurring Earnings Before Interest Expense, Tax, \underline{Minority Income and Equity Earnings}}}{\text{Interest Expense, Including Capitalized Interest}}$$

Income before income taxes	$1,120
Plus interest	180
Adjusted income	$1,300 (A)
Interest expense	$ 180 (B)

(A) $1,300/ (B) $180 = 7.22 times

b.

$$\text{Fixed Charge Coverage} = \frac{\text{Recurring Earnings Before Interest Expense, Tax, Minority Income and Equity Earnings} + \text{\underline{Interest Portion of Rentals}}}{\text{Interest Expense, Including Capitalized Interest} + \text{Interest Portion of Rentals}}$$

Income before income taxes	$1,120
Plus interest	180
Adjusted income	1,300
1/3 of operating lease payments (1/3 x $180)	60
	$1,360

Interest expense	$180
1/3 of operating lease payments	60
	$240

Fixed charge coverage = $\dfrac{\$1,360}{\$\ 240}$ = 5.67 times

2.

The following information is computed from the Fast Food Chain
annual report for 2000:

Current assets	$ 2,731,020	$ 2,364,916
Property and equipment, net	10,960,286	8,516,833
Intangible assets, at cost		
less applicable amortization	294,775	255,919
	$13,986,081	$11,137,668
Current liabilities	$ 3,168,123	$ 2,210,735
Deferred federal income taxes	160,000	26,000
Mortgage note payable	456,000	-
Stockholders' equity	10,201,958	8,900,933
	$13,986,081	$11,137,668
Net sales	$33,410,599	$25,804,285
Cost of goods sold	(30,168,715)	(23,159,745)
Selling and administrative		
expense	(2,000,000)	(1,500,000)
Interest expense	(216,936)	(39,456)
Income tax expense	(400,000)	(300,000
Net Income	$ 624,948	$ 805,084

Note: One-third of the operating lease rental charge was
$100,000 in 2000 and $50,000 in 1999. Capitalized
interest totaled $30,000 in 2000 and $20,000 in 1999.

Required:
a. Based on the above data, for both years, compute:
    1. times interest earned
    2. fixed charge
    3. debt ratio
    4. debt/equity ratio
    5. debt to tangible net worth
b. Comment on the firm's long-term borrowing ability based on
    the analysis.

SOLUTION:

a. 1.

$$\text{Times Interest Earned} = \frac{\text{Recurring Earnings Before Interest Expense, Tax, Minority Income and Equity Earnings}}{\textit{Interest} \text{ Expense, Including Capitalized Interest}}$$

	2000	1999
Net Sales	$33,410,599	$25,804,285
Less Cost of Goods Sold	(30,168,715)	(23,159,745)
Selling and Administrative	(2,000,000)	(1,500,000)
(A)	$ 1,241,884	$ 1,144,540
Interest Expense	$ 216,936	$ 39,456
Capitalized Interest	30,000	20,000
Total Interest (B)	$ 246,936	$ 59,456
(A)/(B)	5.03 times	19.25 times

2. Fixed Charge Interest = $\dfrac{\text{Recurring Earnings Before Interest Expense, Tax, Minority Earnings, Equity Earnings, Plus } \underline{\text{Interest Portion of Rentals}}}{\text{Interest Expense, Including Capitalized Interest, Plus Interest Portion of Rentals}}$

	2000	1999
From Part (1)	$ 1,241,884	$ 1,144,540
Interest Portion of Rentals	100,000	50,000
(A)	$ 1,341,884	$ 1,194,540
From Part (1)	$ 246,936	$ 59,456
Interest Portion of Rentals	100,000	50,000
(B)	$ 346,936	$ 109,456
(A)/(B)	3.87 times	10.91 times

Debt Ratio = $\dfrac{\text{Total Liabilities}}{\text{Total Assets}}$

$ 3,784,123	$ 2,236,735
$13,986,081	$11,137,668
27.1%	20.1%

4. Debt/Equity Ratio = $\dfrac{\text{Total Liabilities}}{\text{Stockholders' Equity}}$

$ 3,784,123	$ 2,236,735
$10,201,958	$ 8,900,933
37.1%	25.1%

5. Debt to Tangible Net Worth = $\dfrac{\text{Total Liabilities}}{\text{Stockholders' Equity} - \text{Intangibles}}$

$\dfrac{\$\ 3,784,123}{\$10,201,958-\$294,775}$ = 38.2% $\dfrac{\$\ 2,236,735}{\$8,900,933-\$\ 255,919}$ = 25.9%

b.   In 2000, this firm had a substantial rise in debt. This included current liabilities, deferred taxes, and a new mortgage note payable. This increased debt and the related increased interest expense caused a decline in interest coverage and a rise in the debt, debt/equity, and debt to tangible net worth ratios. In addition, operating lease rental charges went up, which lowered the fixed charge coverage.

3.
The following financial information is excerpted from the 2000 annual report of Retail Products, Inc.:

Balance Sheet

	(in thousands)	
	2000	1999
Current assets	$ 449,195	$ 433,049
Investments	32,822	55,072
Deferred charges	4,905	12,769
Property, plant and equipment, net	350,921	403,128
Trademarks and leaseholds	45,031	47,004
Excess of cost over fair market value of net assets acquired	272,146	276,639
Assets held for disposal	6,062	10,247
	$1,161,082	$1,237,908
Total liabilities	$ 689,535	$ 721,149
Total Stockholders' Equity	471,547	516,759
	$1,161,082	$1,237,908

Income Statement

Net sales	$2,020,526	$1,841,738
Cost of goods sold	(2,018,436)	(1,787,126)
Selling and administrative	(300,000)	(250,000)
Interest expense	(40,000)	(30,000)
Net income (loss)	($ 337,910)	($ 225,388)

Required:
For each year compute:

a.   1.   Times interest earned
     2.   Debt ratio
     3.   Debt/equity ratio
     4.   Debt to tangible net worth ratio

b. Comment on the results.
c. Does a times interest earned ratio of less than 1 to 1 mean that the firm cannot pay its interest expense?

SOLUTION:

a.

1. Times Interest Earned $=$ $\dfrac{\text{Recurring Earnings Before Interest, Tax, Minority Income and Equity Earnings}}{\text{Interest Expense, Including Capitalized Interest}}$

    <u>2000</u>

    $$\frac{\$2,020,526 - \$2,018,436 - \$300,000}{\$40,000}$$

    Negative 7.45 Times

    <u>1999</u>

    $$\frac{\$1,841,738 - \$1,787,126 - \$250,000}{\$30,000}$$

    Negative 6.51 Times

2. Debt Ratio = $\dfrac{\text{Total Liabilities}}{\text{Total Assets}}$

    <u>2000</u>

    $$\frac{\$\ 689,535}{\$1,161,082}$$

    59.4%

    <u>1999</u>

    $$\frac{\$\ \ 721,149}{\$1,237,908}$$

    58.3%

3. Debt/Equity Ratio = $\dfrac{\text{Total Liabilities}}{\text{Total Stockholders' Equity}}$

    <u>2000</u>

    $$\frac{\$\ 689,535}{\$\ \ 471,547}$$

    146.2%

    <u>1999</u>

    $$\frac{\$\ \ 721,149}{\$\ \ 516,759}$$

    139.6%

4. Debt to Tangible Net Worth Ratio = $\dfrac{\text{Total Liabilities}}{\text{Total Stockholders' Equity} - \text{Intangible Assets}}$

    <u>2000</u>

    $$\frac{\$689,535}{\$471,547-\$45,031-\$272,146} = 446.7\%$$

    <u>1999</u>

    $$\frac{\$721,149}{\$516,759-\$47,004-\$276,639} = 373.4\%$$

7-13

b.   This firm has had a rise in the debt, debt/equity and debt
        to tangible net worth ratios. The debt to tangible net
        worth is especially high due to the high amount of excess
        of cost over fair market value of net assets.

        The times interest earned figure dropped from a negative
        6.51 times in 1999 to a negative 7.45 times in 2000.

        This firm's long-term borrowing ability appears to be very
        negative and deteriorated further in 2000.

c.   No, a times interest earned ratio of less than 1 to 1 does
        not mean, in the short run, that the firm cannot meet its
        interest payments. Some of the expenses, such as
        depreciation, do not require current funds, but they do
        reduce the interest coverage. Also, in the short run, the
        outlay can come from sources of funds other than income.

5.

Mr. Jones has asked you to advise him of the long-term debt
position of Dryden Corporation. He provides you with the ratios
indicated below:

	1998	1999	2000
Fixed Charge Coverage	6.3	4.5	5.0
Times Interest Earned	8.2	6.0	5.3
Debt Ratio	40%	39%	40%
Debt to Tangible Net Worth	80%	81%	84%

Required:
Give the implications and limitations of each item separately and
then the collective inference one may draw about Dryden's long-
term debt-paying ability.

SOLUTION:

Times interest earned has declined. This can be caused by lower
income, higher debt, or a combination of both.

Fixed charge coverage has declined. The decline for this ratio
has been less than the decline in the times interest earned.
This indicates that the use of non-capitalized leases has
declined.

The debt ratio is relatively stable.

The debt to tangible net worth ratio has increased slightly. This
can be caused by higher debt, lower equity, or higher
intangibles.

Since the debt ratio is relatively constant, the problem does
not appear to be higher debt. Rather, higher interest rates or
lower income appear to be the problem. Since the debt ratio is

constant, the most logical explanation for the rise in debt to tangible net worth is a rise in intangibles, which lowers the denominator.

The long-term debt position has declined, but we need more information about the company and industry in order to come to a conclusion on the long-term debt position.

6.

Amsterdam Antiques reported the following comparative income figures in 2000:

	(in thousands)	
	2000	1999
Net sales	$701	$646
Other income	10	8
	711	654
Costs and expenses:		
Cost of goods sold	472	408
Selling and general expenses	176	156
Interest	28	22
	676	586
Income before income taxes and extraordinary items	35	68
Income taxes	(15)	(30)
Income before extraordinary items	20	38
Extraordinary items - losses from fire		18
Net income	$ 20	$ 20

Your boss, the president of Amsterdam bank, is concerned about Amsterdam's borrowing capacity. A representative of Amsterdam Antiques feels that there should be no problem, since net profits are the same with slightly higher sales.

Required:
Compute times interest earned and comment on the bank's position.

SOLUTION:

$$\text{Times Interest Earned:} \quad \frac{\text{Recurring Earnings Before Interest, Tax, Minority Income and Equity Earnings}}{\text{Interest Expense, Including Capitalized Interest}}$$

	2000	1999
Income before income taxes and extraordinary items	$ 35	$ 68
Plus interest expense	28	22
(a)	$ 63	$ 90
(b) Interest expense	$ 28	$ 22
(a) ÷(b)	2.25 times	4.09 times

The ability of the firm to cover its interest has declined substantially due both to rising interest and falling income.

The statement by the Amsterdam Antiques representative is false. The only reason that net income was at $20,000 in 1999 was because of the extraordinary fire loss. Recurring profits dropped from $38,000 to $20,000.

7.

Required:
Following is a list of paired ratios and transactions. For each transaction indicate the effect of that transaction on the specific ratio. Use + for increase, - for decrease, and 0 for no effect.

Transaction	Ratio
a. A firm is required to capitalize leases previously only presented in footnotes.	Debt Ratio of .4
b. A firm sells its own common stock.	Debt/Equity Ratio of 1.12
c. A firm has an increase in selling expense with no change in other expenses.	Times Interest Earned of 6.2 to 1
d. A firm writes off a sizeable account receivable.	Times Interest Earned ratio of 3.6 to 1
e. A firm pays cash for a valuable patent.	Debt to Tangible Net Worth of 1.3 to 1

SOLUTION:

a.	+	d.	0
b.	-	e.	+
c.	-		

8.
Aristocrats Art reported the following trend analysis to its bank as an attachment to a loan application.

	2000	1999	1998
Fixed Charge Ratio	4.00	2.50	1.54
Times Interest Earned	4.94	3.17	2.08
Debt Ratio	.47	.51	.56
Debt to Tangible Net Worth Ratio	.91	1.06	1.36

You have been asked to evaluate the long-term borrowing capacity. You know that a rule of thumb for this industry for the debt/equity ratio is 1 to 1.

Required:
a. Compute the debt/equity ratio for 2000, 1999, and 1998, using the debt ratio as a guide.
b. Comment on the long-term borrowing ability of this firm.

SOLUTION:
a. If total liabilities are .47 of total assets, then total stockholders' equity must be .53, since total liabilities plus total stockholders' equity = total assets.

$$\frac{Debt}{Equity} = \frac{.47}{.53} = 89 \quad (2000$$

$$\frac{.51}{.49} = 1.04 \quad (1999$$

$$\frac{.56}{.44} = 1.27 \quad (1999$$

b. This firm shows evidence of an improved long-term borrowing capacity position. The times interest earned ratio and the fixed charge ratio has improved, as has the debt ratio, debt to tangible net worth ratio, and debt/equity. The debt/equity ratio is now below the industry average.

9.
You have been asked to evaluate the long-term borrowing position of Client, Inc. However, you were given only the following limited information.

Bonds payable, 12%	$1,000,000
Stockholders' equity	1,800,000
Current assets	1,870,000
Tangible assets, net	1,600,000
Intangible assets	40,000
Investments	120,000
Other assets	90,000
Sales	4,000,000
Operating expenses	3,620,000

Required:
Assuming that this is the only information you will receive, estimate the following ratios:
a. Times interest earned
b. Debt ratio
c. Debt/equity ratio
d. Debt to tangible net worth ratio

SOLUTION:
Computations for figures needed in the ratios:

Total assets:
Current assets	$1,870,000
Tangible assets	1,600,000
Intangible assets	40,000
Investments	120,000
Other assets	90,000
Total assets	$3,720,000

Liabilities:
Total assets	$3,720,000
Less stockholders' equity	1,800,000
Total liabilities	$1,920,000

Interest:
$1,000,000 x .12% = $120,000

a. Times Interest Earned $= \dfrac{\text{Recurring Earnings Before Interest, Tax Minority Income and Equity Earnings}}{\text{Interest Expense, Including Capitalized Interest}}$

$$= \frac{\$4,000,000 - \$3,620,000}{\$120,000} = 3.17 \text{ times}$$

b. Debt Ratio $= \dfrac{\text{Total Liabilities}}{\text{Total Assets}}$

$$= \frac{\$1,920,000}{\$3,720,000} = 51.6\%$$

c. Debt/Equity Ratio $= \dfrac{\text{Total Liabilities}}{\text{Shareholders' Equity}}$

$$= \frac{\$1,920,000}{\$1,800,000} = 106.7\%$$

d. Debt to Tangible Net Worth Ratio $= \dfrac{\text{Total Liabilities}}{\text{Shareholders' Equity} - \text{Intangible Assets}}$

$$= \frac{\$1,920,000}{\$1,800,000 - \$40,000} = 109.1\%$$

Required:
Indicate the effect of each of the following transactions on the
ratios listed. Use + to indicate an increase, - to indicate a
decrease, and 0 to indicate no effect. Assume an initial times
interest earned ratio of 3 to 1, and debt ratio of .5 to 1,
debt/equity ratio of 1.0 to 1, and total debt to tangible net
worth ratio of 1.1 to 1.

Transaction	Times Interest Earned	Debt Ratio	Debt Equity Ratio	Total Debt Tangible Net Worth Ratio
a. Collection of accounts receivable.				
b. Firm has decreasing profits due to rising cost of sales.				
c. Firm appropriates a substantial amount for expansion.				
d. Conversion of preferred stock to common.				
e. Repayment of a short-term bank loan (ignore interest).				
f. Payment for a valuable trademark.				
g. The stock is split two for one.				
h. Purchase of equipment financed by a long-term note (consider interest).				
i. Conversion of bonds to stock.				
j. Declaration and payment of cash dividend.				
k. The firm experiences a rise in the rate charged on its line of credit.				

SOLUTION:

Transaction	Times Interest Earned	Debt Ratio	Debt Equity Ratio	Total Debt Tangible Net Worth Ratio
a. Collection of accounts receivable.	0	0	0	0
b. Firm has decreasing profits due to rising cost of sales.	-	-	-	-
c. Firm appropriates a substantial amount for expansion.	0	0	0	0
d. Conversion of preferred stock to common.	0	0	0	0
e. Repayment of a short-term bank loan (ignore interest).	0	-	-	-
f. Payment for a valuable trademark.	0	0	0	+
g. The stock is split two for one.	0	0	0	0
h. Purchase of equipment financed by a long-term note (consider interest).	-	+	+	+
i. Conversion of bonds to stock.	+	-	-	-
j. Declaration and payment of cash dividend.	0	+	+	+
k. The firm experiences a rise in the rate charged on its line of credit.	-	+	+	+

Chapter 8: PROFITABILITY

MULTIPLE CHOICE

c   1.   Which of the following is **not** a base against which
         profits are measured?
         a. owners' equity
         b. owners' and creditors' funds provided
         c. intangibles
         d. revenues
         e. productive assets

a   2.   Net profit margin measures return on:
         a. sales
         b. owners' equity
         c. productive assets
         d. total assets
         e. inventory

b   3.   Total asset turnover measures the ability of a firm to:
         a. generate profits on sales
         b. generate sales through the use of assets
         c. buy new assets
         d. move inventory
         e. cover long-term debt

d   4.   DuPont return on assets uses two component ratios. What
         are they?
         a. inventory turnover x gross profit margin
         b. times interest earned x debt ratio
         c. return on equity x dividend payout
         d. net profit margin x total asset turnover
         e. return on investment x total investment turnover

c   5.   Return on assets **cannot** fall under which of the
         following circumstances?

         Net Profit Margin   Total Asset Turnover
         a. decline   rise
         b. rise   decline
         c. rise   rise
         d. decline   decline
         e. The ratio could fall under all of the above.

a   6.   A reason that equity earnings create a problem in
         analyzing profitability is that equity earnings are:
         a. usually greater than the related cash flow
         b. less than dividends declared
         c. more than dividends declared
         d. extraordinary
         e. non-recurring

c   7. If equity earnings are substantial, in the analysis of profitability, it is advisable to:
   a. consider them as extraordinary
   b. consider them as nonrecurring
   c. investigate the earning power of the parent outside of the related investing activities
   d. recompute the debt ratio and times interest earned to remove the impact of equity earnings
   e. use the DuPont method to lessen the impact of equity earnings

d   8. Which of the following is **not** a type of operating asset?
   a. inventory
   b. cash
   c. land
   d. investments
   e. equipment

d   9. Operating income is:
   a. net sales less cost of goods sold
   b. earnings before interest and tax
   c. earnings before tax and nonrecurring items
   d. gross profit less operating expenses
   e. net income plus interest

b   10. Which of the following circumstances will cause sales to fixed assets to be abnormally high?
   a. a recent purchase of land
   b. a labor-intensive industry
   c. a highly mechanized facility
   d. high direct labor costs from a new union contract
   e. the use of unit-of-production depreciation

d   11. Which of the following ratios will usually have the lowest percent?
   a. return on investment
   b. return on total equity
   c. return on common equity
   d. return on total assets
   e. there is not enough information to tell

e   12. Which suppliers of funds bear the greatest risk and should, therefore, earn the greatest return?
   a. bondholders
   b. suppliers
   c. general creditors such as banks
   d. preferred shareholders
   e. common shareholders

b   13.   Gross profit margin is an important ratio of merchandising firms because:
      a.   their investments in real property are high
      b.   cost of goods sold is usually the largest expense
      c.   selling expenses, like advertising, are usually quite high
      d.   it measures their ability to collect receivables
      e.   it measures their ability to use total assets

b   14.   Segment reporting requires presentation of information on a segmented basis. Which factor does **not** have to be reported?
      a.   identifiable assets
      b.   allocation of common costs
      c.   sales
      d.   depletion, depreciation, and amortization
      e.   capital expenditures

d   15.   Which of the following is **not** a requirement of FASB No. 14 in segment reporting?
      a.   data on foreign operations by geographic area
      b.   data on export sales
      c.   data on major customers
      d.   information to determine how the specific segments were identified
      e.   identification of the industry if a company operates primarily in only one such industry

c   16.   Which of the following is **not** a reporting requirement on interim reports?
      a.   seasonal information
      b.   major changes in income tax provision
      c.   full although condensed balance sheet
      d.   earnings per share
      e.   significant changes in financial position

b   17.   Income tax expense in interim reporting should:
      a.   be based on the quarterly income only
      b.   contain a judgment estimation of the annual effective tax rate
      c.   be based on the income year-to-date
      d.   exclude extraordinary items in earlier quarters of the year
      e.   disregard year-end adjustments

d   18.   Minority share of earnings is:
      a.   the total earnings of unconsolidated subsidiaries
      b.   earnings based on the percent of holdings by parent the of unconsolidated subsidiaries
      c.   the total earnings of consolidated subsidiaries
      d.   earnings based on the percent of holdings by outside owners of consolidated subsidiaries
      e.   none of the above

c   19.   Net earnings before deducting minority share of earnings
           is utilized in the following ratios, since minority
           interests are included in the base. Which ratio is an
           exception to this statement?
           a.   net profit margin
           b.   return on assets
           c.   return on equity
           d.   return on investment
           e.   none of the above

d   20.   Which of the following would most likely cause a rise in
           net profit margin?
           a.   increased sales
           b.   decreased preferred dividends
           c.   increased cost of sales
           d.   decreased operating expenses
           e.   decreased earnings per share

e   21.   Which of the following could cause return on assets to
           decline when net profit margin is increasing?
           a.   sale of investments at year-end
           b.   increased turnover of operating assets
           c.   decline in book value
           d.   a stock split
           e.   purchase of a new building at year-end

c   22.   Which of the following expresses DuPont analysis?
           a.   net profit margin = total asset turnover times
                return on assets
           b.   total asset turnover = operating asset turnover
                times financial leverage
           c.   return on assets = net profit margin times total
                asset turnover
           d.   return on investment = return on equity (1 - tax
                rate)
           e.   dividend yield = dividend payout times earnings per
                share

b   23.   Operating assets equals:
           a.   cash, accounts receivable, and equipment
           b.   current assets plus tangible assets
           c.   total assets minus intangible assets
           d.   only long-term assets
           e.   only current assets

c   24.   Return on investment measures:
           a.   return to all suppliers of funds
           b.   return to all long-term creditors
           c.   return to all long-term suppliers of funds
           d.   return to stockholders
           e.   return to all short-term suppliers of funds

c   25.   In the formula for return on investment, interest
            expense is multiplied by (1 - tax rate). Why is this
            adjustment made?
            a.   Interest is not tax deductible.
            b.   Debt is excluded from the denominator.
            c.   Net income, in the formula, is after tax.
            d.   Dividends are not deductible for tax purposes.
            e.   none of the above

TRUE/FALSE

T   1.   Profitability is the ability of the firm to generate
           earnings.

F   2.   In profitability analysis, absolute numbers are more
           meaningful than relative numbers because the analyst
           needs to know if one firm earned more dollars than the
           other.

F   3.   Net profit margin is net profit before minority share of
           earnings and nonrecurring items to total assets.

T   4.   The use of debt with high interest charges may cause the
           net profit margin to be low.

T   5.   High fixed costs in a period of low activity can cause a
           low net profit margin.

F   6.   DuPont analysis breaks return on assets into net profit
           margin and borrowing capacity.

T   7.   Either a drop in net profit margin or a drop in total
           asset turnover, or both, can cause return on assets to
           fall.

F   8.   Equity earnings are usually lower than the cash
           generated from the investment as dividends.

F   9.   Operating assets exclude investments, land, and
           intangibles from the asset base.

T   10.   The operating ratios may give significantly different
           results from net earnings ratios if a firm has large
           amounts of nonoperating assets generating income.

T   11.   DuPont analysis can be done with net income or operating
           income figures as long as the related asset base is
           consistent.

F   12.   Sales to fixed assets will have the least meaning if
           assets are relatively new.

T   13.   Return on investment measures the return on long-term
           suppliers of funds.

T   14. Return on investment will typically be lower than return on equity.

F   15. Redeemable preferred stock is best considered as equity for ratio analysis.

T   16. Changes in the cost of goods sold can have a substantial impact on gross profit margin.

F   17. In order to compute gross profit margin, the income statement must be in single-step format.

T   18. Ratios of profits to sales and to identifiable assets can help to analyze profitability by segment.

T   19. Segment data contain information about geographic markets, including foreign countries.

T   20. An interim period is a fiscal period less than one year.

T   21. Interim reporting recognizes that timeliness of data offsets lack of detail and requires only minimum data.

F   22. Interim reports are usually audited.

T   23. Interim reports are useful in analyzing the impact of seasonality.

T   24. Interim reports cover fiscal periods of less than one year.

T   25. The SEC requires interim financial data on Form 10-Q.

PROBLEMS

1.

Required:
Indicate the effect of the transactions listed below on each of
the following: working capital, current ratio, debt ratio, net
income, stockholders' equity. Use + to indicate an increase, -
to indicate a decrease and 0 to indicate no effect. Assume an
initial current ratio of more than 1 to 1.

Transaction	Working Capital	Current Ratio	Debt Ratio	Net Income	Stockholder's Equity
a. A cash dividend is declared and paid.					
b. Cash is obtained through long-term bank loans. (Do not consider interest).					
c. Equipment is pur-purchased with short-term notes. (Do not consider interest.)					
d. Merchandise is purchased on credit.					
e. A fixed asset is sold for more than book value.					
f. A stock split takes effect.					
g. Current operating expenses not pre-viously recognized are paid.					
h. A firm makes a long-term cash investment in the stock of a consolidated subsidiary.					
i. A firm recognizes depreciation expense.					
j. A firm refinances short-term notes with long-term notes. (Ignore interest.)					

SOLUTION:

Transaction	Working Capital	Current Ratio	Debt Ratio	Net Income	Stock-holders Equity
a. A cash dividend is declared and paid.	-	-	+	0	-
b. Cash is obtained through long-term bank loans. (Do not consider interest).	+	+	+	0	0
c. Equipment is purchased with short-term notes. (Do not consider interest.)	-	-	+	0	0
d. Merchandise is purchased on credit.	0	-	+	0	0
e. A fixed asset is sold for more than book value.	+	+	-	+	+
f. A stock split takes effect.	0	0	0	0	0
g. Current operating expenses not previously recognized are paid.	-	-	+	-	-
h. A firm makes a long-term cash investment in the stock of a consolidated subsidiary.	-	-	0	0	0
i. A firm recognizes depreciation expense.	0	0	+	-	-
j. A firm refinances short-term notes with long-term notes. (Ignore interest.)	+	+	0	0	0

2.

DuBois, Inc. experienced the following trend in operating profit ratios for the five years ended in 2001.

	Operating Income Margin	Return on Operating Assets
2001	9.7%	12.2%
2000	9.3%	11.5%
1999	9.1%	11.2%
1998	8.8%	10.6%
1997	8.6%	10.1%

Required:
Using the DuPont analysis, determine whether the trend in turnover increased the return on operating assets or lowered it.

SOLUTION:

	Return on Operating Assets	=	Operating Income Margin	x	Operating Asset Turnover
2001	12.2%	=	9.7%	x	1.26
2000	11.5%	=	9.3%	x	1.24
1999	11.2%	=	9.1%	x	1.23
1998	10.6%	=	8.8%	x	1.20
1997	10.1%	=	8.6%	x	1.17

Operating asset turnover has risen. This helped increase the rate of growth of return on operating assets.

3.

Fluctuation, Inc. recorded the following profit figures in 1999-2001:

	2001	2000	1999
Net sales	$30,500	$25,600	$22,900
Costs and expenses:			
Cost of products sold	12,600	10,300	8,350
Selling	7,875	5,025	4,580
General	2,950	2,325	2,150
Research and development	4,100	3,190	2,840
	$27,525	$20,840	$17,920
Operating income	$ 2,975	$ 4,760	$ 4,980
Other income (expense)	525	(300)	(400)
Earnings before tax	3,500	4,460	4,580
Income tax	1,480	1,990	2,100
Net income	$ 2,020	$ 2,470	$ 2,480

Required:
a.   Compute the net profit margin for 1999-2001
b.   Compute the gross profit margin for 1999-2001
c.   Describe the trend in profitability and pinpoint its causes.

SOLUTION:

a.   Net Profit Margin =

Net Income Before Minority Share of Earnings and Non-recurring items	2001	2000	1999
	$ 2,020	$ 2,470	$ 2,480
Net Sales	$30,500	$25,600	$22,900
	6.62%	9.65%	10.83%

b.   Gross Profit Margin =

	$30,500	$25,600	$22,900
	-12,600	10,300	8,350
Gross Profit	$17,900	$15,300	$14,550
Sales	$30,500	$25,600	$22,900
	58.69%	59.77%	63.54%

c.   Both net profit margin and gross profit margin have declined in the three years. A major factor has been the rising cost of goods which causes gross profit to fall. Selling expenses, general expenses, and research and development expenses have all increased in relation to net sales.

Selling	25.82%	19.63%	20.00%
General	9.67	9.08	9.39
R & D	13.44	12.46	12.40

Selling expenses, in particular, impaired 2001 profit.

4.

The following are extracted from the financial statements of
Frem, Inc. for 2001, 2000, and 1999:

	2001	2000	1999
Net sales	$233,000	$204,000	
Cost of sales	(124,000)	(110,000)	
Selling and administrative expenses	(95,000)	(81,500)	
Other income:			
Interest	(3,700)	(3,050)	
Other	100	1,175	
Earnings before tax and extraordinary credit	10,400	10,625	
Provision for income tax	(4,800)	(4,740)	
Earnings before extraordinary credit	5,600	5,885	
Extraordinary credit	--	1,510	
	$ 5,600	$ 7,395	
Total assets	$202,000	$173,000	$161,000
Long-term debt	24,600	17,400	15,200
Common equity	123,000	116,800	112,800
Preferred stock (Not redeemable)	4,000	4,000	4,000
Preferred dividends	280	280	280

(assume these are the only equity accounts)

Required:
a. Compute the following ratios for 2001 and 2000.   _2 each_
     1.   Net profit margin
     2.   Total asset turnover
     3.   Return on assets
     4.   Return on investment
     5.   Return on total equity
     6.   Return on common equity
     7.   Gross profit margin

b.   Discuss the trend in profitability and identify specific
     causes for the trend.

SOLUTION:
a.   2001   2000
  1.   Net Profit Margin   =

Net Income Before Minority Share of Earnings and Nonrecurring Items	$ 5,600	$ 5,885
Net Sales	$233,000	$204,000
=	2.40%	2.88%

2.   Total Asset Turnover =

Net Sales	$233,000	$204,000
Average Total Assets	$202,000 + $173,000 / 2	$173,000 + $161,000) / 2

| | 1.24 times | 1.22 times |

3.   Return On Assets   =
Net Income Before Minority Share

of Earnings and Nonrecurring Items	$ 5,600	$ 5,885
Average Total Assets	$187,500	$167,000

| = | 2.99% | 3.52% |

4.   Return On Investment =
Net Income Before Minority Share
of Earnings and Nonrecurring Items
+ (Interest Expense) x (1-Tax Rate)
Average (Long-Term Liabilities +
     Equity)

Net income before extraordinary item	$ 5,600	$ 5,885
Interest expense	3,700	3,050

Tax rate:
  2001:

$ 4,800	=		
$10,400		46.15%	

  2000:

$ 4,740	=		
$10,625			44.61%

Interest expense * (1-t)	1,992	1,689

Net income before extraordinary
item + interest expense (1-t)

(5,600 + 1,992) [A]	7,592	
(5,885 + 1,689) [A]		7,574

Long-term liabilities and stockholders' equity:
Beginning of year:

Long-term debt	$ 17,400	$ 15,200
Common equity	116,800	112,800
Preferred stock	4,000	4,000

End of year:

Long-term debt	24,600	17,400
Common equity	123,000	116,800
Preferred stock	4,000	4,000

Total	$289,800	$270,200
Average	[B] 144,900	135,100

Return on investment [A]/[B]	5.24%	5.61%

5. Return on Equity =

$$\frac{\text{Net Income Before Nonrecurring Items - Dividends on Redeemable Preferred Stock}}{\text{Average Total Equity}}$$

Net income before non-recurring Items – Dividends on Redeemable preferred stock [A]		$ 5,600	$ 5,885
Total equity:			
Beginning of year			
Common equity		116,800	112,800
Preferred stock		4,000	4,000
End of year:			
Common stock		123,000	116,800
Preferred stock		4,000	4,000
Total		247,800	237,600
Average	[B]	123,900	118,800
Return on total equity [A]/[B]		4.52%	4.95%

6. Return on Common equity =

Net Income Before Nonrecurring
Items - Preferred Dividends
Average Common Equity

Net income before non-recurring items		$ 5,600	$ 5,885
Less: Preferred dividends		280	280
Numerator	[A]	5,320	5,605
Total common equity:			
Beginning of year		116,800	112,800
End of year		123,000	116,800
Total		239,800	229,600
Average	[B]	119,900	114,800
Return on Common Equity [A]/[B]		4.44%	4.88%

7. Gross Profit Margin =			
Net Sales	[B]	$233,000	$204,000
Cost of Sales		-124,000	-110,000
Gross Profit	[A]	$109,000	$ 94,000
	[A]/[B]	46.78%	46.08%

b.   Net profit margin, return on total assets, return on investment, return on total equity, and return on common equity have declined. Total asset turnover and gross profit margin rose slightly. The problem appears to be in selling and administrative expenses, other income, and taxes, since gross profit margin rose.

Of particular concern is the very low return to common shareholders. It is lower than return on total equity and investment, which indicates that preferred owners and creditors, who bear less risk, ar getting a higher return.

5.
The following data are taken from the financial statements of Motorise, Inc. for 2001 and 2000.

	2001	2000
Net sales	$ 65,000	$ 61,000
Equity income (dividends: $65,$62)	320	365
Total	65,320	61,365
Total expenses, including taxes	63,800	59,700
Net income	$ 1,520	$ 1,665
Total assets	$ 32,200	$ 30,600
Investment (using equity method)	3,800	2,800

Required:
a.   Compute the following ratios for both years, using total net income and assets. Use ending balance sheet figures.
1. net profit margin
2. return on total assets (use year-end total assets)
b.   Recompute the ratios, removing the effect of equity income on investments. (For return on total assets, use year-end total assets.
c.   Discuss the change. Why is it advisable to remove equity earnings in this case?

SOLUTION:

a.

	2001	2000
1. Net Profit Margin =		

	2001	2000
Net Income Before Minority Share of Earnings and Nonrecurring Iems / Net Sales	$1,520 / $65,000	$1,665 / $61,000
	2.34%	2.73%

2.   Return on Total Assets   =

	2001	2000
Net Income Before Minority Share of Earnings and Nonrecurring Items / Average Total Assets	$1,520 / $32,200	$1,665 / $30,600
	4.72%	5.44%

b. Remove equity earnings and investments:

1. Net Profit Margin =

$$\frac{\text{Net Income Before Minority Share of Earnings and Nonrecurring Items}}{\text{Net Total Assets}} \qquad \frac{\$1,520 - \$320}{\$65,000} \qquad \frac{\$1,665 - \$365}{\$61,000}$$

$$1.85\% \qquad 2.13\%$$

2. Return on Total Assets =

$$\frac{\text{Net Income Before Minority Share of Earnings and Nonrecurring Items}}{\text{Net Total Assets}} \qquad \frac{\$1,200}{\$32,200 - \$3,800} \qquad \frac{\$1,300}{\$30,600 - \$2,800}$$

$$4.23\% \qquad 4.68\%$$

. The return on investments is clearly higher in terms of equity income because the ratios drop when the effect is removed. The trend stays the same, however. The main reason for removing equity earnings is that they do not represent cash flow, since dividends are much lower.

.

The following is the summary quarterly financial data for Communico, Inc. (unaudited). Communico ends its year on March 1.

2001	June 30	Sept 30	Dec 31	March 31
Sales	$2,100,000	$2,350,000	$2,350,000	$3,700,000
Gross profit	905,000	930,000	1,090,000	1,600,000
Net income	90,000	220,000	290,000	550,000
Earnings per share	.78	.88	1.10	1.55

2000				
Sales	$1,280,000	$1,700,000	$1,700,000	$3,000,000
Gross profit	440,000	650,000	880,000	1,500,000
Net income	88,000	185,000	240,000	500,000
Earnings per share	.44	.93	1.20	2.50

Required:
. Discuss the concept of seasonality raised by these data.
. Does it appear that this firm uses a natural business year?

SOLUTION:

. This firm clearly operates with a seasonal pattern. Its busiest time, represented both by sales and profits, is January-March. Each quarter of the year builds up to this.

. This firm clearly uses a natural business year, counting inventory after peak sales, when inventory is at its lowest.

7.

The following is segment data for Audio-Visual Corporation:

(in thousands)	2001	2000	1999
Revenues:			
Broadcasting Division	$1,500	$1,100	$ 880
Records Division	1,050	780	510
Book Division	450	380	210
Total	$3,000	$2,260	$1,600
Profits:			
Broadcasting Division	$ 270	$ 226	$ 175
Records Division	72	95	68
Book Division	41	28	18
Total	$ 383	$ 349	$ 261
Identifiable Assets:			
Broadcasting Division	$ 600	$ 380	$ 280
Records Division	560	450	300
Book Division	300	240	160
Total	$ 1,460	$ 1,070	$ 740
Capital Outlays:			
Broadcasting Division	$ 40	$ 25	$ 20
Records Division	28	20	11
Book Division	12	10	5
Total	$ 80	$ 55	$ 36

Required:
a.   Compute profit/revenues and profit/assets for the three divisions and
     in total for all three years.
b.   Discuss your findings.
c.   Evaluate this firm's capital expenditure policy, given the results i
     parts a and b.

SOLUTION:

		2001	2000	1999
a.	Profit : Broadcasting	$ 270	$ 226	$ 175
	Revenues	$1,500	$1,100	$ 880
		18.00%	20.55%	19.89%
	Records	$ 72	$ 95	$ 68
		$1,050	$ 780	$ 510
		6.86%	12.18%	13.33%
	Book	$ 41	$ 28	$ 18
		$ 450	$ 380	$ 210
		9.11%	7.37%	8.57%
	Total	$ 383	$ 349	$ 261
		$3,000	$2,260	$1,600
		12.77%	15.44%	16.31%

8-16

		2001	2000	1999
Profit:	Broadcasting	$ 270	$ 226	$ 175
Assets		$ 600	$ 380	$ 280
		45.00%	59.47%	62.50%
	Records	$ 72	$ 95	$ 68
		$ 560	$ 450	$ 300
		12.86%	21.11%	22.67%
	Book	$ 41	$ 28	$ 18
		$ 300	$ 240	$ 160
		13.67%	11.67%	11.25%
	Total	$ 383	$ 349	$ 261
		$1,460	$1,070	$ 740
		26.23%	32.62%	35.27%

The overall trend in profit/revenue and profit assets for this firm is downward, with the biggest drop in 2001. The major cause of this is the declining profitability in the record division. Lower profit margins in broadcasting also have an impact, especially since this is the biggest division.

One way to answer this is to look at capital outlays/identifiable assets.

	2001	2000	1999
Broadcasting	$ 40	$ 25	$ 20
	$ 600	$ 380	$ 280
	6.67%	6.58%	7.14%
Records	$ 28	$ 20	$ 11
	$ 560	$ 450	$ 300
	5.00%	4.44%	3.67%
Book	$ 12	$ 10	$ 5
	$ 300	$ 240	$ 160
	4.00%	4.17%	3.13%

The high profit ratio would support expansion in broadcasting where capital outlays as a percent of assets are highest. However, the drop in profitability in records does not support a rising rate of expenditures to assets.

The increasing expenditure in the book segment can likely be justified by the improved profitability of this segment.

8.

The Friendly Bookstore has experienced rapid growth since its formation i
1997. Following is selected data from its annual report.

	2001	2000	1999	1998	1997
Sales	$1,500,000	$1,260,000	$970,000	$840,000	$600,000
Cost of Sales	1,008,000	971,000	598,000	515,000	360,000
Net Profit	60,000	53,000	46,000	39,000	30,000
Total Assets	1,489,000	1,100,000	897,000	768,000	545,000
Number of Books Sold	97,500	85,703	73,192	63,200	45,187

Required:
a.   Perform a horizontal common-size analysis of the data given, using
     1997 as the base year.
b.   Comment on the results.

SOLUTION:

a.

	2001	2000	1999	1998	1997
Sales	250.0%	210.0%	161.7%	140.0%	100.0%
Cost of Sales	280.0%	269.7%	166.1%	143.1%	100.0%
Net Profit	200.0%	176.7%	153.3%	130.0%	100.0%
Total Assets	273.2%	201.8%	164.6%	140.9%	100.0%
Number of Books Sold	215.8%	189.7%	162.0%	139.9%	100.0%

b.   Sales have grown rapidly but at a slower rate than costs of sales.
     This has caused a lower rate of profit growth.

     Assets have grown faster than sales, indicating that the firm is
     generating less sales per dollar of assets. It is also generating
     less profit on assets, since profits grew much more slowly than
     assets.

     The number of books sold has grown less rapidly than total sales.
     This indicates a rise in selling price per book sold.

Condensed comparative financial statements for the Woodstock Manufacturing Company appear below:

Balance Sheets
April 30
(In thousands of dollars)

	2001	2000	1999
Assets:			
Current assets	$ 1,700	$ 1,120	$ 1,544
Plant and equipment (net)	8,110	7,830	5,404
Other assets	1,004	695	772
Total assets	$10,814	$ 9,645	$ 7,720
Liabilities and Stockholders' Equity:			
Current liabilities	$ 950	$ 880	$ 772
Long-term liabilities	2,023	1,591	1,544
Capital stock ($10 par)	4,600	4,600	3,000
Paid-in capital in excess			
of par	770	770	386
Retained earnings	2,471	1,804	2,018
Total liabilities and			
stockholders' equity	$10,814	$ 9,645	$ 7,720

Income Statements
For the Years Ended April 30
(in thousands of dollars)

	2001	2000	1999
Net sales	$38,610	$32,175	$25,740
Cost of sales	25,100	19,950	15,400
Gross profit	13,510	12,225	10,340
Selling expenses	7,700	6,565	5,148
Administrative expenses	4,270	4,175	3,861
Total operating expenses	11,970	10,740	9,009
Operating income	1,540	1,485	1,331
Interest expense	115	95	100
Net income before tax	1,425	1,390	1,231
Income taxes	655	645	541
Net income	$ 770	$ 745	$ 690

Required:
Perform a horizontal common-size analysis of the balance sheet items, using 1999 as the base year. Also include a horizontal analysis of sales and net income. Comment on significant trends and relationships revealed by the computations.

SOLUTION:

	2001	2000	1999
Assets:			
Current assets	110.1	72.5	100.0%
Plant and equipment (net)	150.1	144.9	100.0%
Other assets	130.1	90.0	100.0%
Total assets	140.1	124.9	100.0%
Liabilities and Stockholders' Equity:			
Current liabilities	123.1	114.0	100.0%
Long-term liabilities	131.0	103.0	100.0%
Capital stock ($10 par)	153.3	153.3	100.0%
Paid-in capital in excess of par	199.5	199.5	100.0%
Retained earnings	122.4	89.4	100.0%
Total Liabilities and Stockholders' equity	140.1	124.9	100.0%
Sales	150.0	125.0	100.0%
Net Income	111.6	108.0	100.0%

In 2000, the firm had a significant increase in plant and equipment. Ther
was also a substantial rise in common stock and paid-in capital.
Apparently, the expansion was primarily financed by a stock sale.

From 2000 to 2001, there is a substantial rise in current assets, from a
drop in 2000. There also is a large rise in long-term liabilities.

Sales have risen faster than assets, indicating increased turnover.
However, profits have risen much more slowly than sales. In 2000, the fi
must have paid substantial dividends, since retained earnings declined,
despite the net income.

10.

Condensed comparative financial statements for Woodstock Manufacturing
Company appear below:

	2001	2000	1999
Assets:			
Current assets	$1,700	$1,120	$1,544
Plant and equipment/net	8,110	7,830	5,404
Total assets	1,004	695	772
	10,814	$9,645	$7,720
Liabilities and Stockholders' Equity:			
Current liabilities	$ 950	$ 880	$ 772
Long-term liabilities	2,023	1,591	1,544
Capital stock ($10 par)	4,600	4,600	3,000
Paid-in capital in excess of par	770	770	389
Retained earnings	2,471	1,804	2,018
Total liabilities and stockholders' equity	$10,814	$9,645	$7,720

Income Statement
For the Years Ended April 30
(In thousands of dollars)

	2001	2000	1999
Net sales	$38,610	$32,175	$25,740
Cost of sales	25,100	19,950	15,400
Gross profit	13,510	12,225	10,340
Selling expenses	7,700	6,565	5,148
Administrative expenses	4,270	4,175	3,861
Total operating expenses	11,970	10,740	9,009
Operating income	1,540	1,485	1,331
Interest expense	115	95	100
Net income before tax	1,425	1,390	1,231
Income taxes	655	645	541
Net income	$ 770	$ 745	$ 690

Required:
Perform a vertical common size analysis of the income statement. Comment on significant trends.

	2001	2000	1999
Net sales	100.0%	100.0%	100.0%
Cost of sales	65.0	62.0	59.8
Gross profit	35.0	38.0	40.2
Selling expenses	19.9	20.4	20.0
Administrative expenses	11.1	13.0	15.0
Total operating expenses	31.0	33.4	35.0
Operating income	4.0	4.6	5.2
Interest expense	.3	.3	.4
Net income before tax	3.7	4.3	4.8
Income taxes	1.7	2.0	2.1
Net income	2.0%	2.3%	2.7%

Although absolute profits have risen, the profit margin on sales has
declined steadily. The principal cause of the decline is increased cost of
sales. Cost of sales have risen from 59.8% to 65.0%. This increase is
offset by declining selling and administrative costs in relation to sales.
Taxes as a percent of sales also have declined.

. .

On the left is a list of terms related to trend analysis and other types of
financial information and services. On the right are descriptions and
definitions of these terms.

Required:
Match each term to its best description by placing the correct number before the term.

___ a.	Vertical common-size statement.	1.	Full or partial statements expressed in percentages of a given base.
___ b.	Segment reporting	2.	Requires full financial statements on a Quarterly basis
___ c.	Interim reporting	3.	All statement figures are expressed as a percentage of a base figure from that year's statement.
___ d.	Trend analysis	4.	A breakdown by major lines of business, only required in reporting.
___ e.	Common-size	5.	A breakdown by major lines of business.
___ f.	Horizontal	6.	All statement figures are expressed as a percentage of base-year figures.
		7.	Requires estimation of some expense items.
		8.	A comparison of financial data over time.
		9.	Visual aids to understanding financial data.

SOLUTION:

a.   ___3___   d.   ___8___
b.   ___5___   e.   ___1___
c.   ___7___   f.   ___6___

Descriptions/definitions not used are 2, 4, and 9.

2.

The Clothes Clutch, a retail clothier, has had average sales of $400,000 for the last five years, 1997-2001. The firm's total assets at the end of 2001 were $400,000.

An internal staff cost analyst has prepared the following financial data from the annual reports. You have been hired as a consultant to help analyze the financial position.

	2001	2000	1999	1998	1997
Current Ratio	2.80	2.43	2.36	2.10	2.00
Acid Test Ratio	2.03	1.93	1.82	1.61	1.47
Days' Sales in Receivables	61	58	54	42	35
Merchandise Inventory Turnover	4.2	4.1	4.1	3.9	3.7
Debt Ratio	.48	.50	.49	.47	.47
Times Interest Earned	4.6	4.8	5.9	5.7	6.0
Sales as a % of 1994 Sales	1.46	1.23	1.12	1.06	1.00
Net Income as a % of 1994 Income	1.31	1.20	1.10	1.06	1.00
Gross Profit Margin	38.5%	38.8%	38.9%	40.0%	39.7%
Operating Expenses to Net Sales	11.4%	11.3%	11.5%	11.4%	11.7%
Net Profit Margin	7.6%	8.6%	8.9%	9.4%	9.3%
Return on Total Assets	9.4%	9.6%	9.6%	10.0%	10.7%

Required:
. Explain the trend in liquidity. Make specific reference to the effect of receivables and inventory on this trend.
. Briefly describe the trend in the long-term debt-paying ability of The Clothes Clutch. Explain the cause(s) of this trend.
. The net profit margin has declined substantially. Cite and discuss specific causes of this.
. Has the firm utilized its total assets effectively? Discuss the ability of the firm to generate sales based on total assets.
. Specifically cite and briefly describe two additional types of information that would aid in your analysis.

SOLUTION:

. Both the current ratio and acid-test ratio have risen. This might appear, initially, to be a good sign. However, days' sales in receivables have nearly doubled, indicating a worsening problem in the collection of receivables. This problem could cause the rise in the current ratio and acid- test ratio.

Merchandise inventory turnover has increased, although not substantially. This indicates better movement of inventory. Overall, liquidity appears to be good, but not as good as it appears based on the current ratio and acid- test ratio because receivables appear to create a liquidity problem.

b.   Two measures of long-term debt-paying ability are given. The debt
      ratio appears to be relatively stable. However, the times interest
      earned ratio has declined. This indicates that the firm is not
      covering its debt as well as it did previously. This decrease could
      restrict its future borrowing power.

c.   Gross profit margin has declined slightly, indicating a slight rise
      the cost of goods sold. Operating expenses to net sales has remained
      relatively stable. Other causes of the decline could be other income
      and expense items, such as interest expense. Problems with interest
      were already indicated in times interest earned.

d.   This question calls for use of DuPont analysis, specifically turnover
      Students may need a hint to this effect.

	Return on Total Assets	=	Net Profit Margin	x	Total Asset Turnover
2001	9.4	=	7.6	x	1.24
2000	9.6	=	8.6	x	1.12
1999	9.6	=	8.9	x	1.08
1998	10.0	=	9.4	x	1.06
1997	10.7	=	9.3	x	1.15

This computation shows that part of the decline in net profit margin
between 1997 and 2001 has been offset by increased turnover. Increased
turnover indicates more efficient use of assets to generate sales
dollars.

e.   Almost any type of additional data would be of help. Some of the
      better suggestions are:

            Common-size analysis
            Industry statistics
            The cash flow statement
            Other specific ratios
            Segment data
            Data for competition

Chapter 9: FOR THE INVESTOR

MULTIPLE CHOICE

c   1. The ratio percentage of earnings retained is the same as that termed:
  a. dividend yield
  b. dividend payout
  c. this year's retained earnings to income
  d. return on common equity
  e. book value

a   2. The earnings per share is computed for:
  a. common stock
  b. nonredeemable preferred
  c. redeemable preferred
  d. common stock and nonredeemable preferred stock
  e. common stock and fully diluted preferred stock

d   3. In 2001, ABC Company reported earnings per share of $2.00 for 10,000 shares. In 2002, there was a 2-for-1 stock split, for which 2002 earnings per share were reported at $2.10. The appropriate earnings per share presentation for a 2-year comparative analysis would be:

	2002	2001
a.	$2.10	$2.00
b.	$1.05	$2.00
c.	$1.05	$2.00
d.	$2.10	$1.00
e.	none of the above	

e   4. Interest expense creates magnification of earnings through financial leverage because:
  a. the interest rate is variable
  b. interest accompanies debt financing
  c. the use of interest causes higher earnings
  d. interest costs are cheaper than the required rate of return to equity owners
  e. while earnings available to pay interest rise, earnings to residual owners rise faster

d   5. What is the effect of the exercise of stock options?
  a. They generate cash to the issuing firm and, therefore, increase profit per share.
  b. They are an expense at the time of exercise. This lowers net income.
  c. They increase debt and lower borrowing capacity but have no effect on profit.
  d. They increase the number of shares outstanding and may dilute earnings per share.
  e. They have no immediate effect on profitability.

b   6. A summarized income statement for Leveraged Inc. is
            presented below.

Sales	$1,000,000
Cost of Sales	600,000
Gross Profit	400,000
Operating Expenses	250,000
Operating Income	150,000
Interest Expense	30,000
Earnings Before Tax	120,000
Income Tax	40,000
Net Income	$ 80,000

The degree of financial leverage is:
a. $150,000/$30,000
b. $150,000/$120,000
c. $1,000,000/$400,000
d. $150,000/$80,000
e. $400,000/$120,000

a   7. Dawn Alive reported the following for 2001:

Ending market price	$40.75
Earnings per share:	
Basic	$ 2.50
Diluted	$ 2.08
Dividends per share	$ 1.10

The price/earnings ratio and dividend payout were:
a. 19.59 and 52.88%
b. 16.30 and 52.88%
c. 16.30 and 44.00%
d. 19.59 and 44.00%
e. 37.04 and 52.88%

e   8. The best dividend payout ratio:
            a.   approximates 50%
            b. continues at the same level as was historically paid
            c. is similar to the industry average
            d. is higher than that of competitors
            e. does not follow any rule of thumb for dividend
               payout

c 9. The following data were gathered from the annual report of Desk Products:

Market price per share	$ 30.00
Number of common shares	10,000
Preferred stock, 5%	
$100 par	$ 10,000
Common equity	$140,000

The book value per share is:
a. $30.00
b. $15.00
c. $14.00
d. $13.75
e.   none of the above

e 10. Which of the following is **not** a reason to interpret book value with caution?
a.   Land may be worth more than it cost.
b.   Depreciable assets may be held.
c.   Investments may be worth more than their purchase price.
d.   Patents may have a high market value.
e.   All of the above.

e 11. Which of the following is **not** a true statement regarding stock options?
a.   They may cause dilution of earnings per share.
b.   They generally allow the purchase of common stock at favorable terms.
c.   They sometimes involve a compensation expense.
d.   Exercise improves the short-term liquidity and debt position of the issuing firm.
e.   The potential dilution can be disregarded in financial analysis.

c 12. Good Boss Inc. had the following pattern of results related to stock appreciation rights:

Shares in the plan	20,000
Option price	$15.00
Market price -	
end year 1	$20.00
end year 2	$18.00
end year 3	$22.00

The compensation expense would be:

	Year 1	2	3
a.	$100,000	-0-	$40,000
b.	$100,000	$60,000	$40,000
c.	$100,000	(40,000)	$80,000
d.	$400,000	-0-	$40,000
e.	none of the above		

c 13. Using financial leverage is a good financial strategy from the viewpoint of stockholders of companies having:
   a. a high debt ratio
   b. cyclical highs and lows
   c. steady or rising profits
   d. a steadily declining current ratio
   e. none of the above

e 14. A firm has a degree of financial leverage of 1.20. If earnings before interest and tax increase by 20%, then net income:
   a. will not necessarily change
   b. will increase by 20%
   c. will decrease by 24%
   d. will decrease by 20%
   e. none of the above

b 15. The price/earnings ratio:
   a. measures the past earning ability of the firm
   b. is a gauge of future earning power as seen by investors
   c. relates price to dividends
   d. relates price to total net income
   e. all of the above

c 16. Stable dividend policy would most commonly imply:
   a. a high price/earnings ratio
   b. a stable dividend yield
   c. stable dividends per share
   d. stable earnings per share
   e. increasing dividends per share

c 17. Book value per share may **not** approximate market value per share because:
   a. the book value is after tax
   b. book values are based on replacement costs rather than market values
   c. book value is related to book figures and market value is related to the future potential as seen by investors
   d. investors do not understand book value
   e. book value is not related to dividends

TRUE/FALSE

F 1. The percentage of earnings retained is computed by dividing retained earnings by total stockholders' equity.

T 2. In computing earnings per share, preferred dividends are subtracted from net income.

T   3. Nonrecurring items such as extraordinary income and disposal of a segment require separate earnings per share disclosure.

T   4. When a stock split occurs, earnings per share must be adjusted retroactively.

F   5. The use of debt financing creates financial leverage.

F   6. The degree of financial leverage is the multiplication factor by which debt to equity changes as new debt is issued.

T   7. The higher the amount of interest expense, the higher the degree of financial leverage.

F   8. The price/earnings ratio expresses the relationship between selling prices of the company's products and the related earnings.

T   9. A firm might have a low dividend payout ratio if it were planning a major expansion.

T   10. Dividend yield relates dividends per share to market price per share.

T   11. Total earnings from securities include both dividends and price appreciation.

F   12. Book value per share measures the current value of the net assets on a per share basis.

F   13. When market value is below book value, this relationship indicates that the investors view the company as having strong future potential.

T   14. Stock appreciation rights give the employee compensation at a future date, based on the market price at the date of exercise in excess of a pre-established dollar market.

T   15. Stock appreciation rights will usually impact more on reported earnings than on stock options.

T   16. The impact of stock options is included in the earnings per share computation.

T   17. Operating leverage refers to the existence of fixed operating costs.

F   18. A disadvantage of interest expense over dividends is its tax deductibility.

F   19. If financial leverage is used, a rise in EBIT will cause a lessor rise in net income.

F   20.   In general, new firms, growing firms, and firms
           perceived as growth firms will have a relatively low
           percentage of earnings retained.

PROBLEMS

1.

Listed below in the left column is a specific ratio. In the
right column is a business transaction.

Ratio	Transaction
a. Earnings per share	Issued a stock dividend.
b. Dividend yield	High earnings causes a substantial rise in market price of the common stock.
c. Earnings per share	Collect accounts receivable.
d. Net profit margin	Experienced a substantial rise in cost of goods sold.
e. Book value per share	The firm experiences a net loss.
f. Return on equity	The firm has a 10% increase in profit.
g. Book value per share	The firm has a 2 for 1 stock split.
h. Return on assets	Net income increases 20%.

Required:
Indicate the effect of this transaction on the given ratio. Use
+ for increase, - for decrease, and 0 for no effect.

SOLUTION:

a.	-	e.	-
b.	-	f.	+
c.	0	g.	-
d.	-	h.	+

2.

In 2002, Revelation, Inc. reported the following statistics:

	2002	2001
Basic Per Share	$3.60	$2.70

In 2003, their comparative earnings per share were reported as follows:

	2003	2002*	2001
Basic Per Share	$3.61	$3.00	$2.25

However, the footnote referred to by the asterisk (*) was inadvertently omitted. You are informed that the firm is basically the same and that there has been no change in accounting principle.

Required:
a. What information should have been reported in the missing footnote?
b. Should the price/earnings ratio be changed by the transaction that caused the change in earnings per share?
c. List two other profit-related measures other than earnings per share that would be changed because of this transaction.

SOLUTION:

a. The firm issued a 20% stock dividend that required restating its earnings.

$$\$3.60 \div x = \$3.00$$
$$x = 1.2$$

b. No. Theoretically the price should be lowered by the same percentage as earnings; therefore, there is no change in the relative price/earnings.

c. Dividends per share, book value per share.

3.

Comparative data for Albers Automotive for the two-year period 2001-2002 are presented below:

Income Statement Data

	2002	2001
Net Sales	$1,500,000	$1,200,000
Cost of Goods Sold	934,000	741,000
Gross Profit	566,000	459,000
Operating Expense	376,000	277,000
Operating Income	190,000	182,000
Other Expense (interest)	15,000	12,000
Earnings Before Income Tax	175,000	170,000
Income Taxes	66,000	71,000
Net Income	$ 109,000	$ 99,000
Dividends Paid	48,000	42,000
Net Increase in Retained Earnings	$ 61,000	$ 57,000

Balance Sheet Data

Assets		2002		2001
Cash	$	30,000	$	10,000
Receivables (net)		130,000		90,000
Inventory		170,000		113,000
Land, Buildings, and Equipment (net)		650,000		547,000
Intangible Assets		20,000		20,000
		$1,000,000	$	780,000

Liabilities and Stockholders' Equity

		2002		2001
Trade Notes and Accounts Payable	$	100,000	$	40,000
Miscellaneous Current Liabilities		50,000		11,000
5% Bonds Payable		300,000		240,000
Common Stock, $10 Par		100,000		100,000
Additional Paid-In Capital		51,000		51,000
Retained Earnings		399,000		338,000
		$1,000,000	$	780,000

Market price of stock end-of-each year. $ 81 $ 68

Required:
a. Compute the following ratios for both years.
    1. net profit margin
    2. total asset turnover (use year-end assets)
    3. return on assets (use year-end assets)
    4. operating income margin
    5. operating asset turnover (use year-end assets)
    6. return on operating assets (use year-end assets)
    7. return on investment (use year-end long-term debt and
        stockholders equity)
    8. return on total equity (use year-end total equity)
    9. basic earnings per share
    10. degree of financial leverage
    11. price/earnings ratio
    12. dividend payout ratio
    13. dividend yield
b. Perform a DuPont analysis for both years, using both net
    profit and operating income. Comment on the results.
c. Comment on the trend in profitability as indicated by the
    ratios given.
d. Why is return on investment lower than return on equity?
e. Describe the firm's dividend policy. Could this be related
    to market price?

SOLUTION:

		2002	2001

a. 1.   Net Profit Margin:

$$\frac{\text{Net Income Before Minority Share of Earnings and Non - Recurring Items}}{\text{Net Sales}}$$

	2002	2001
	$109,000	$99,000
	$1,500,000	$1,200,000
	7.3%	8.3%

2.   Total Asset Turnover:

$$\frac{\text{Net Sales}}{\text{Total Assets}}$$

	2002	2001
	$1,500,000	$1,200,000
	$1,000,000	$780,000
	1.50 times	1.54 times

3.   Return on Assets:

$$\frac{\text{Net Income Before Minority Share of Eanrings and Non - Recurring Items}}{\text{Total Assets}}$$

	2002	2001
	$109,000	$99,000
	$1,000,000	$780,000
	10.9%	12.7%

4.   Operating Income Margin:

$$\frac{\text{Operating Income}}{\text{Net Sales}}$$

	2002	2001
	$190,000	$182,000
	$1,500,000	$1,200,000
	12.7%	15.2%

5.   Operating Asset Turnover:

$$\frac{\text{Net Sales}}{\text{Operating Assets}}$$

	2002	2001
	$1,500,000	$1,200,000
	$1,000,000 - $20,000	$780,000 - $20,000
	1.53 times	1.58 times

6.   Return on Operating Assets:

$$\frac{\text{Operating Income}}{\text{Operating Assets}}$$

	2002	2001
Operating Income	$190,000	$182,000
Operating Assets	$980,000	$760,000
	19.4%	23.9%

7.   Return on Investment:

$$\frac{\text{Net Income + Interest(1 - tax rate}}{\text{Long - Term Debt Plus Stockholders' Equity}}$$

Net Income	$ 109,000	$ 99,000
Interest	15,000	12,000
Earnings Before Tax	175,000	170,000
Income Tax	66,000	71,000
Tax Rate	37.7%	41.8%
1-Tax Rate	62.3%	58.2%
Interest (1-tax rate)	9,345	6,984
Net Income+Interest (1-tax rate) [a]	118,345	105,984
Long-Term Debt	300,000	240,000
Stockholders' Equity	550,000	489,000
Long-Term Debt + Stock-holders' Equity [b]	850,000	729,000
Return on Investment [a]÷[b]	13.9%	14.5%

8. Return on Total Equity:

$$\frac{\text{Net Income Before Non - Recurring Items - Dividends on Redeemable Preferred Stock}}{\text{Total Equity}}$$

Net Income Before Non - Recurring Items - Dividends on Redeemable Preferred Stock	$109,000	$99,000
Total Equity	$550,000	$489,000
	19.8%	20.2%

9. Basic Earnings Per Share:

Net Income - Preferred Dividends	$109,000	$99,000
Average Number of Common Shares Outstanding	$10,000	$10,000
	$10.90	$9.90

10. Degree of Financial Leverage:

Earnings Before Interest, Tax, Minority Share of Earnings, Equity Income, and Non-Recurring Items	$190,000	$182,000
Earnings Before Tax, Minority Share of Earnings	$175,000	$170,000
	1.09	1.07

11. Price/Earnings Ratio:

Market Price	$81.00	$68.00
Basic Earnings Per Share	$10.90	$ 9.90
	7.43 times	6.87 times

12. Dividend Payout Ratio:

<u>Dividends Per Common Share</u>	<u>$ 4.80</u>	<u>$4.20</u>
Earnings Per Share	$10.90	$9.90
	44.0%	42.4%

13. Dividend Yield:

<u>Dividends Per Common Share</u>	<u>$4.80</u>	<u>$4.20</u>
Market Price Per Common Share	$81.00	$68.00
	5.9%	6.2%

b. Return on Assets = Net Profit Margin x Total Asset Turnover

2002: 10.9%*	=	7.3%	x	1.5
2001: 12.7%*	=	8.3%	x	1.54

Return on Operating assets = Operating Income Margin x Operating Asset Turnover

2002: 19.4%*	=	12.7%	x	1.53
2001: 23.9%*	=	15.2%	x	1.58

*(rounding may cause slight differences)

From 2001 to 2002, both return on asset and return on operating assets have declined. This is caused by both a decline in margin and turnover.

c. Although absolute profit has increased, most relative measures of profit have declined. A faster rise in sales than profits has caused a decline in profit margins. Turnovers have declined slightly.

Returns on investment and equity have declined, due to faster rises in the bases than in profits. Earnings per share have increased.

The degree of financial leverage has risen slightly. The rise in market price has increased the price/earnings ratio. This is a good sign of investor confidence.

Dividend payout is up slightly, but dividend yield is down, due to the higher market price.

Book value has risen, but it is still lower than the market price.

d. Return on investment is lower than return on equity because the cost of debt is lower than the cost of equity.

e. The firm has increased its dividends faster than earnings, as evidenced by a rising dividend payout. This may have helped cause the rise in market price.

4.
Columbia Inc. reported the following financial data in its December 31, 2002 report to shareholders:

Preferred Stock, 8%, $100 Par	$ 40,000
Common Stock, $10 par, 20,000 Shares	
Issued and Outstanding	200,000
Paid-In Capital in Excess of Par	160,000
Retained Earnings	170,000

In 2003, the firm reported the following (presented in partial form):

Operating income	$120,000
Interest expense	30,000
Earnings before tax	90,000
Tax	40,000
Net Income	$ 50,000

On July 15, 2003, the common stock was split 2 for 1. The common stock dividends were declared and paid as follows:

1st Quarter	$.28
2nd Quarter	$.28
3rd Quarter	$.15
4th Quarter	$.15

The year-end market price for 2003 was $18.00

Required:
For 2003, compute:
a. earnings per share
b. dividends per share based on ending shares
c. the degree of financial leverage
d. percentage of earnings retained
e. dividend payout
f. dividend yield
g. price/earnings ratio
h. book value per share

SOLUTION:
a. Earnings Per Share =
$$\frac{}{\text{Common Shares Outstanding}}$$
(after split)
= $1.17

b. Dividends Per Share

1st	$.14	Adjusted for split
2nd	.14	Adjusted for split
3rd	.15	
4th	.15	
	$.58	

c. Degree of Financial
    Leverage $= \dfrac{\text{EBIT}}{\text{EBT}} = \dfrac{\$120,000}{\$\ 90,000} = 1.33$

d. Percentage of

   $\text{Earnings Retained} = \dfrac{\text{Net Income - Dividends}}{\text{Net Income}} = \dfrac{\$50,000 - (\$3,200 + \$23,200)}{\$50,000}$

   $= 47.20\%$

e. Dividend Payout $= \dfrac{\text{Dividends Per Common Share}}{\text{Earnings Per Share}} = \dfrac{\$\ .58}{\$1.17}$

   $= 49.57\%$

f. Dividend Yield $= \dfrac{\text{Dividends Per Common Share}}{\text{Market Price Per Share}} = \dfrac{\$\ .58}{\$18.00}$

   $= 3.2\%$

g. Price/Earnings
   Ratio $= \dfrac{\text{Market Price Per Common Share}}{\text{Earnings Per Share}} = \dfrac{\$18.00}{\$\ 1.17}$

   $= 15.38$ times

h. Book Value Per
   Share $= \dfrac{\text{Common Equity}}{\text{Common Shares Outstanding}}$

Beginning Retained Earnings		$170,000
+ Net Income		50,000
		220,000
- Dividends		26,400
		193,600
Plus: Common Stock		200,000
Paid-In Capital		160,000
Total Common Equity	[A]	$553,600
Common Shares	[B]	40,000
Book Value	[A]/[B]	$13.84

5.

Company P had the following capital structure at year-end after closing:

6% Bonds	$10,000,000
3% Preferred Stock	20,000,000
Common Stock ($10 par)	10,000,000
Paid in Capital in Excess of Par	15,000,000
Retained Earnings	35,000,000

Required:

a. The return on common equity was 9%. Determine the net income.

b. Using your answer in (a), compute return on investment. Assume that the bond interest is the only interest expense and the tax rate is 50%. Use year-end balance sheet figures.

c. Compute basic per share. Assume the same number of common shares throughout the whole year.

d. Compute book value per share

e. If the market value is $78, compute the price/earnings ratio, using your answer to part (c).

f. Would you expect the market price to be higher than the book value per share?

SOLUTION:

a. Return on Common Equity = $\dfrac{\text{Net Income - Preferred Dividends}}{\text{Common Shareholders' Equity}}$

$\dfrac{x - \$600,000}{\$60,000,000}$ = 9%

$x - \$600,000$ = $5,400,000

x = $6,000,000

b. Return on Investment = $\dfrac{\text{Net Income + Interest Expense} (1 - \text{tax rate})}{\text{Long-Term Debt + Stockholders' Equity}}$

Net Income	$ 6,000,000
Interest Expense	$ 600,000
Interest Expense x (1 - tax rate)	$ 300,000
Net Income + Interest Expense x (1 - tax rate)	$ 6,300,000
Long-Term Debt + Stockholders' Equity	$90,000,000

Return on Investment = $\dfrac{\$ 6,300,000}{\$90,000,000}$ = 7%

c. Basic Earnings Per Share = $\dfrac{\text{Net Income - Preferred Dividends}}{\text{Number of Common Shares Outstanding}}$

= $\dfrac{\$6,000,000 - \$600,000}{1,000,000 \text{ shares}}$

= $5.40/share

Shares are computed by dividing common stock of $10,000,000 by $10 par.

d.   Book Value Per Share = $\dfrac{\text{Common Equity}}{\text{Number of Common Shares outstanding}}$

$$= \dfrac{\$60,000,000}{1,000,000}$$

$$= \$60.00$$

e.   Price/Earnings Ratio $= \dfrac{\$78.00}{\$ 5.40} = 14.4 \text{ times}$

f.   The market price is usually higher than the book value per share.

6.

In 19X1, Firm X has net income of $182,000, income tax of $80,000, and interest expense of $31,000.

Required:
a.   Compute the degree of financial leverage.

b.   If in 19X2, earnings before interest and tax increase by 10%, what should be the change in net income?

c.   If in 19X2, earnings before interest and tax decline by 50%, what should be the change in net income?

SOLUTION:

a.   Net Income $182,000
     Income Tax   80,000
     Earnings Before Tax   262,000
     Interest Expense   31,000
     Earnings Before Interest
       and Tax $293,000

     Degree of Financial Leverage $= \dfrac{\text{Earnings Before Interest and Tax}}{\text{Earnings Before Tax}}$

     $$= \dfrac{\$293,000}{\$262,000} = 1.12$$

b.   If earnings before interest and tax increase by 10%, net income should increase by 1.12 times 10%, or 11.2%.

c.   If earnings before interest and tax decrease by 50%, net income should decrease by 1.12 times 50%, or decline of 56%.

7.

Jazzy Juniors, a retail clothing manufacturer, reported the
following profit figures in its 2002 annual report:

	2002	2001
Earnings Before Extraordinary Items	$1,726,010	$1,646,117
Extraordinary Loss, Net of Tax (Note 1)	(346,106)	-
Net Income	$1,379,904	$1,646,117
Basic Earnings Per Share:		
Before Extraordinary Items	$3.13	$2.99
Extraordinary loss, Net of Tax	(.63)	-
Net Income	$2.50	$2.99

Note 1 - On September 3, the firm experienced a substantial fire
loss. The uninsured portion of the loss was $547,910.
This loss reduced income taxes by $201,804.

Required:
a. You have been asked to project 2003 earnings for Jazzy
Juniors. Your research indicates that a 12% rise in
earnings is reasonable. Compute the estimated earnings and
basic earnings per share. Explain your answer.

b. Compute the number of shares of common stock outstanding in
2002, using net income and basic earnings per share of $2.50.
Note: There is no preferred stock outstanding.

c. Why are the taxes on the casualty loss presented with the
loss rather than with income taxes.

SOLUTION:

a. The casualty loss would not be expected to recur. Therefore,
the profit estimate should be based on earnings before
extraordinary items.

$$\$1,726,010 \times 1.12 = \$1,933,131$$
$$\text{Per Share} \quad \$3.13 \times 1.12 = \$3.51$$

b. Basic Per Share = $\dfrac{\text{Net Income - Preferred Dividends}}{\text{Number of Common Shares}}$

$$\$2.50 = \frac{\$1,379,904}{x}$$

$$x = \frac{\$1,379,904}{2.50}$$

$$x = 551,961.60$$

c. The taxes are presented with the loss to separate them from
recurring tax expense, based on recurring profit.

8.

The following data relate to the Sparrow Company for the current year:

Income before extraordinary item	$6,000,000
Less: Preferred stock dividends	100,000
Income available to common stockholders	5,900,000
Extraordinary item	(900,000)
Net income available to common stockholders	$5,000,000
Common shares outstanding on January 1	3,000,000
Issuance of common stock on October 1	400,000

Note: The Sparrow Company uses the calendar year.

Required:
a. Compute the weighted-average share.

b. Compute the basic EPS for:
   1. Income before extraordinary item
   2. Extraordinary item
   3. Net income

SOLUTION:

a.

Dates Outstanding	Shares Outstanding	Fraction of Period	Weighted Average Shares
January 1-September 30	3,000,000	3/4	2,250,000
October 1-December 31	3,400,000	1/4	850,000
Weighted-average shares			3,100,000

b. Basic EPS for:

1. Income Before Extraordinary Item $1.90

$$\frac{\$5,900,000}{3,100,000} = \$1.903$$

2. Extraordinary Item 29¢

$$\frac{\$900,000}{3,100,000} = .290$$

3. Net Income $1.61

$$\frac{\$5,000,000}{3,100,000} = \$1.613$$

Chapter 10: STATEMENT OF CASH FLOWS

MULTIPLE CHOICE

e   1.   Which of the following is **not** a purpose of the statement
         of cash flows?
         a.   to show cash flow from operations
         b.   to show cash flow from financing activities
         c.   to show cash flow from investing activities
         d.   to show all investing and financing transactions
         e.   to show operating expenses for a period of time

e   2.   Which of the following is **not** a typical cash flow under
         operating activities?
         a.   cash inflows from sale of goods or services
         b.   cash inflows from interest
         c.   cash outflows to employees
         d.   cash outflows to suppliers
         e.   cash inflows from sale of property, plant, and
              equipment

c   3.   Which of the following is **not** a typical cash flow under
         investing activities?
         a.   cash inflow from receipt of loans
         b.   cash inflow from sale of property, plant, and
              equipment
         c.   cash outflow for payment of amounts borrowed
         d.   cash outflow for loans to other entities
         e.   cash outflow for purchase of property, plant, and
              equipment

d   4.   Which of the following is **not** a typical cash flow under
         financing activities?
         a.   cash inflow from sale of equity securities
         b.   cash inflow from sale of bonds
         c.   cash outflow for payment of dividends
         d.   cash outflow for loans to other entities
         e.   cash outflow for payment of amounts borrowed

c   5.   Working capital is defined as:
         a.   total assets less intangible assets
         b.   current assets divided by current liabilities
         c.   current assets less current liabilities
         d.   total assets less current assets
         e.   current assets less liabilities

c   6.   Amortization of patents can be added to income in the
         operations section of the statement of cash flows:
         a.   because it is not a tax deductible expense
         b.   because it results in a cash inflow
         c.   because it does not require the outlay of funds
         d.   because patent amortization is not an expense
         e.   because it represents an inflow of cash

d   7. Which of the following is **not** an item added back to income in the operations section of the statement of cash flows when using the indirect presentation?
        a. depreciation
        b. amortization of goodwill
        c. increase in deferred income taxes
        d. amortization of bond premium
        e. amortization of patents

b   8. Which of the following transactions is **not** reflected in a statement of cash flows?
        a. sale of treasury stock
        b. declaration of a stock dividend
        c. purchase of foreign subsidiary with cash
        d. issuance of convertible bonds
        e. purchase of equipment with cash

e   9. Management should **not** use the statement of cash flows for which of the following purposes?
        a. to determine dividend policy
        b. to determine cash flow from operations
        c. to determine cash flow from investing activities
        d. to determine cash flow from financing activities
        e. to determine the balance in accounts receivable

a   10. Tim Company had sales of $30,000, increase in accounts payable of $5,000, decrease in accounts receivable of $1,000, increase in inventories of $4,000, and depreciation expense of $4,000. What was the cash collected from customers?
        a. $31,000
        b. $35,000
        c. $34,000
        d. $25,000
        e. $26,000

b   11. Conroy Company had sales of $50,000, increase in accounts payable of $4,000, decrease in accounts receivable of $3,000, tax expense of $5,000, and an increase in taxes payable of $1,000. What was the cash outflow for taxes?
        a. $54,000
        b. $4,000
        c. $6,000
        d. $53,000
        e. $45,000

c   12. Francis Company had operating expenses of $20,000,
         depreciation expense of $4,000. What was the cash paid
         for operating expenses?
         a. $24,000
         b. $22,000
         c. $21,500
         d. $20,400
         e. $23,000

d   13. In a statement of cash flows (indirect method),
         depreciation expense should be presented as a (an):
         a. cash flow from financing activities
         b. cash flow from investing activities
         c. deduction from net income
         d. addition to net income
         e. financial activity

a   14. The retirement of debt by the issuance of common stock
         should be presented in a statement of cash flows in
         which of the following sections?
         a. supplemental schedule of noncash investing and
             financing activities
         b. cash flows from operating activities
         c. cash flows from investing activities
         d. cash flows from financing activities
         e. supplemental schedule to reconcile net income to net
             cash provided by operations

d   15. The statement of cash flows became a required statement
         in which year?
         a. 1995
         b. 1978
         c. 1971
         d. 1988
         e. 1993

e   16. Which of the following should **not** be considered as part
         of "cash and cash equivalents?"
         a. cash on hand
         b. cash on deposit
         c. highly liquid investments
         d. investments in short-term securities
         e. cash restricted for retirement of bonds

c   17. Which of the following accounts will **not** be considered
         when computing cash flow from operations?
         a. accounts receivable
         b. inventories
         c. equipment
         d. accounts payable
         e. taxes payable

e   18.   Which of the following accounts is **not** part of working
           capital?
           a.   cash
           b.   accounts receivable
           c.   inventory
           d.   accounts payable
           e.   investments

b   19.   Which of the following is used as the focus for the
           current statement that presents a change in funds?
           a.   cash
           b.   cash and cash equivalents
           c.   current assets
           d.   working capital
           e.   none of the above

TRUE/FALSE

T   1.   When the funds statement is presented on a working
           capital basis, the cash flow of a company may not be
           obvious.

T   2.   Working capital is considered to be one of the prime
           indicators of liquidity.

T   3.   The income statement will not fairly represent the funds
           from operations

T   4.   Depreciation expense reduces operating income but does
           not require the use of funds.

F   5.   With the indirect method of presenting cash from
           operations, the income statement is essentially
           presented on a cash basis.

F   6.   A cash outflow will be generated by an increase in a
           liability.

T   7.   Within an individual account, there may be an
           explanation of both a source and a use of cash.

F   8.   The cash flow/current maturities of long-term debt and
           current notes payable is a ratio that indicates long-
           term debt-paying ability.

F   9.   The cash flow/total debt ratio is one that indicates a
           firm's ability to meet its current maturities of debt.

T   10.   Cash flow per share is usually higher than earnings per
           share.

T   11.   Cash flow per share is a better indication of a firm's
           ability to make capital expenditure decisions and pay
           dividends than is earnings per share.

F   12.   Cash flow per share can be viewed as a substitute for earnings per share in terms of a firm's profitability.

T   13.   The statement of cash flows should be reviewed for several time periods in order to determine the major sources of cash and the major uses of cash.

F   14.   Only cash flow transactions are presented in the statement of cash flows, including supporting schedules.

T   15.   The conversion of long-term bonds into common stock is an example of a transaction involving two financing activities with no cash flow effect.

PROBLEMS

1.
The statement of cash flows was added as a required financial statement to overcome deficiencies of the income statement and balance sheet.

Required:
Briefly describe the purpose of each of these three financial statements. Indicate in your answer how the statement of cash flows helped overcome the shortcomings of the other two statements.

SOLUTION:

The income statement presents revenues, expenses, and earnings for a given period of time. The balance sheet presents assets, liabilities, and equity at the end of the fiscal period. The statement of cash flows presents inflows and outflows of cash categorized as operating, investing, and financing. Neither the income statement nor the balance sheet provide information on cash flows.

2.

Required:
Indicate the effect of each of the following transactions on (a) cash and (b) working capital. Use + to indicate an increase, - to indicate a decrease, and 0 for no effect.

a.   Collect accounts receivable
b.   Recognize depreciation expense
c.   Pay taxes payable
d.   Purchase fixed assets for cash
e.   Sell common stock
f.   Realize cash surrender value of officer's life insurance
g.   Increase deferred income taxes (long-term liability)
h.   Amortize premium on bonds payable

SOLUTION:

	Cash	Working Capital
a.	+	0
b.	0	0
c.	-	0
d.	-	-
e.	+	+
f.	+	+
g.	0	0
h.	0	0

3.

Required:
Indicate whether each of the following would be under Operating
(O), Investing (I), Financing (F), or whether the item would not
appear (N) on the statement of cash flows.

a. Purchase of treasury stock
b. Sale of marketable securities above cost
c. Net loss
d. Issuance of bonds payable for cash
e. Sale of equipment at less than book value
f. Sale of inventory for cash
g. Issuance of long-term debt for cash
h. Exercise of stock options by officers
i. Payment of cash dividend
j. Collection of accounts receivable

SOLUTION:

a.	F	e.	I	i.	F
b.	O	f.	O	j.	O
c.	O	g.	F		
d.	F	h.	F		

4.

Required:
Place an X in the appropriate columns for each of the situations.

Situation	Operating Activity	Investing Activity	Financing Activity	Effect on Cash +	Effect on Cash -	Non-Cash Trans-action
a. Paying off accounts payable						
b. Issuance of bonds for cash						
c. Sale of land for Cash						
d. Retirement of common stock with cash						
e. Acquired land for common stock						
f. Decrease in inventory						

SOLUTION:

Situation	Operating Activity	Investing Activity	Financing Activity	Effect on Cash +	Effect on Cash -	Non-Cash Transaction
a. Paying off accounts payable	X				X	
b. Issuance of bonds for cash			X	X		
c. Sale of land for Cash		X		X		
d. Retirement of common stock with cash			X		X	
e. Acquired land for common stock		X	X			X
f. Decrease in inventory	X			X		

5.

The Jones Clothing Store presented the following statement of
cash flows for the year ended December 31, 2001.

Jones Clothing Store
Statement of Cash Flows
For the Year Ended December 31, 2001

	Cash received:	
a.	From sales to customers	$200,000
b.	Interest income	10,000
c.	Loans from banks	50,000
d.	From sale of property, plant, and equipment	100,000
e.	From issuance of common stock	150,000
f.	From issuance of bonds	100,000
	Total cash received	$610,000
	Cash payments:	
g.	For dividends	$ 20,000
h.	For purchase of stock of another company	150,000
i.	For purchase of equipment	200,000
j.	For acquisition of inventory	80,000
k.	To employees	60,000
	Total cash payments	$510,000
	Net increase in cash	$100,000

Required:
a.   Prepare a statement of cash flows in proper form.
b.   Comment on the major flows of cash.

SOLUTION:

a.

Jones Clothing Store
Statement of Cash Flows
For the Year ended December 31, 2001

Cash flows from operating activities:
Received from sales to customers	$200,000
Interest income received	10,000
Payment for inventory	(80,000)
Payment to employees	(60,000)
Net increase from operating activities	70,000

Cash flows from investing activities:
Received from sale of property, plant and equipment	100,000
Payment for stock of another company	(150,000)
Payment for purchase of equipment	(200,000)
Net decrease from investing activities	(250,000)

Cash flows from financing activities
Received from loans from bank	50,000
From issuance of common stock	150,000
From issuance of bonds	100,000
Payment of dividends	(20,000)
Net increase from financing activities	280,000

Net increase in cash	$100,000

b. Jones Clothing Store had a major inflow of funds from
    financing activities of $280,000 and a major outflow of
    funds for investing activities of $250,000. Operating
    activities generated a net increase of $70,000.

6.

The balance sheet for December 31, 2001, and December 31, 2000,
and the income statement for the year ended December 31, 2001, of
the Rocket Company follow:

Rocket Company
Balance Sheet
December 31, 2001 and 2000

	2001	2000
Assets		
Cash	$ 25,000	$20,000
Accounts receivable, net	60,000	70,000
Inventory	80,000	100,000
Land	50,000	50,000
Building and equipment	130,000	115,000
Accumulated depreciation	(85,000)	(70,000)
Total assets	$260,000	$285,000

Liabilities and Stockholders' Equity

Accounts payable	$ 30,000	$ 35,000
Income taxes payable	4,000	3,000
Wages payable	5,000	3,000
Current notes payable	50,000	60,000
Common stock	110,000	100,000
Retained earnings	61,000	84,000
Total liabilities and stockholders' equity	$260,000	$285,000

Rocket Company
Income Statement
For the Year Ended December 31, 2001

Sales		$500,000
Less expenses:		
Cost of goods sold	330,000	
Selling and administrative expenses	90,000	
(includes depreciation of $15,000)		
Interest expense	5,000	
Total expenses		425,000
Income before taxes		75,000
Income tax expense		30,000
Net income		$45,000

Note: Cash dividends of $68,000 were paid during 2001.

Required:
a. Prepare the statement of cash flows for 2001.
    (Present cash flows from operations, using the indirect
    approach.)
b. Compute the ratio cash flow/current maturities of long-term
    debt and current notes payable.
c. Comment on the statement of cash flows and the ratio
    computed in (b).

SOLUTION:

a.

Rocket Company
Statement of Cash Flows
For the Year Ended December 31, 2001

```
Cash flow from operating activities:
Net income                                       $45,000
Add/(deduct) items not affecting
    operating cash:
  Depreciation expense                            15,000
  Decrease in receivables                         10,000
  Decrease in inventory                           20,000
  Accounts payable decrease                       (5,000)
  Income taxes payable increase                    1,000
  Wages payable increase                           2,000
Net increase in cash flow from operations        $88,000


Cash flow from investing activities:
    Cash payments for building                   (15,000)


Cash flow from financing activities:
    Cash from issuance of stock                   10,000
    Cash paid for retirement of notes
        payable                                  (10,000)
    Cash dividends paid                          (68,000)
Net cash outflow from financing
    activities                                   (68,000)

Net increase in cash                           $ 5,000
```

b. Cash from operations/Current maturities of long-term debt and
    current notes payable

$$\frac{\$88,000}{\$50,000} = 1.76 \text{ times}$$

c. Significant cash inflow came from operating activities
    ($88,000), while significant outflow went to financing
    activities ($68,000). Most of the outflow for financing
    activities went for dividends ($68,000).

    Cash from operations/current maturities of long-term debt,
    and current notes payable was 1.76 times. This indicates
    significant liquidity from operations.

7.

The following statements are presented for Melvin Company:

Melvin Company
Balance Sheets
December 31, 2001, and 2000

Assets	2001	2000
Cash	$ 625	$ 499
Marketable securities,	260	370
Trade accounts receivable, less allowances		
of 36 in 2001 and 18 in 2000	1,080	820
Inventories, fifo	930	870
Prepaid expenses	230	220
Total current assets	$3,125	$2,779
Investments	820	600
Property, plant, and equipment:		
Land	130	127
Buildings and improvements	760	670
Machinery and equipment	2,100	1,400
	2,990	2,197
Less allowances for depreciation	1,100	890
	1,890	1,307
Goodwill	500	550
Total assets	$6,335	$5,236
Liabilities and Shareholders' Equity		
Accounts payable	$1,200	$ 900
Accrued payroll	100	80
Accrued taxes	300	200
Total current liabilities	1,600	1,180
Long-term debt	900	750
Deferred income taxes	300	280
Shareholders' equity:		
Common stock	1,000	1,000
Retained earnings	2,535	2,026
Total liabilities and shareholders' equity	$6,335	$5,236

Melvin Company
Statement of Income
For the Year Ended December 31, 2001

Net sales	$8,000
Cost of goods sold	3,900
Gross profit	4,100
Selling, administrative, and general expenses	2,600
Operating income	1,500
Interest expense	100
Income before income taxes	1,400
Income taxes	400
Net income	$1,000
Net income per share	$2.00

Note: 500 shares of common stock were outstanding.

Melvin Company
Statement of Cash Flows
For the Year Ended December 31, 2001

Cash flows from operating activities:		
Net income		$1,000
Adjustments to reconcile net income to net		
cash provided by operating activities:		
Depreciation	$210	
Amortization	50	
Increase in accounts receivable	<260>	
Increase in inventories	< 60>	
Increase in prepaid expenses	< 10>	
Increase in accounts payable	300	
Increase in accrued payroll	20	
Increase in accrued taxes	100	350
Net cash provided by operating activities		1,350
Cash flows from investing activities:		
Outflow for investments	<220>	
Outflow for property, plant, and		
equipment	<793>	
Net cash outflow for investing activities		<1,013>
Cash flows from financing activities:		
Inflow from issuance of bonds	150	
Inflow from deferred taxes	20	
Dividends paid	<491>	
Net cash outflow for investing activities		< 321>
Net increase in cash and cash equivalents		$ 16

Required:
a. Compute the following ratios for 2001:
     1. working capital
     2. current ratio
     3. acid-test ratio (conservative)

4. operating cash flow/current maturities of long-term debt and current notes payable
5. operating cash flow/total debt
6. operating cash flow per share

b. Review the statement of cash flows and comment on significant items.

c. 1. Which items appearing on the cash flow statement do not directly represent cash flow?
   2. Why are these items disclosed on the cash flow statement?

SOLUTION:

a. 1. Working Capital:

$$\$3,125 - \$1,600 = \$1,525$$

2. Current Ratio = Current Assets/Current Liabilities

$$\frac{\$3,125}{\$1,600} = 1.95$$

3. Acid-Test Ratio = $\dfrac{\text{Cash Equivalents + Marketable Securities + Net Receivables}}{\text{Current Liabilities}}$

$$\frac{\$625 + \$260 + \$1,080}{\$1,600} = \frac{\$1,965}{\$1,600} = 1.23$$

4. OperatingCash Flow/Current Maturities of Long-Term Debt and Current Notes Payable

$$\$1,350/0 = \text{Infinity}$$

5. Operating Cash Flow/Total Debt

$$\$1,350/\$2,800 = .48$$

6. Operating Cash Flow Per Share = $\dfrac{\text{Cash Flow - Preferred Dividends}}{\text{Common Shares Outstanding}}$

$$\frac{\$1,350 - \$0}{500} = 2.70$$

b. Net cash provided by operating activities was $1,350, cash outflow for investing was $1,013, and net cash outflow for financing activities was $321. Dividends represent 49% of income and 36% of cash provided by operating activities. Cash outflow for property, plant, and equipment was significant in relation to cash provided by operations.

c.   1.   Depreciation, amortization.
     2.   The cash flows from operating activities is presented
          using the indirect approach. This approach starts with
          net income and adjusts to net cash provided by operating
          activities. Since the non-cash items of depreciation and
          amortization have been considered to be expenses on the
          income statement, they need to be added back.

8.

The income statement and other selected data for Pat Gibson
Company is shown below.

Pat Gibson Company
Accrual Basis Income Statement
For the Year Ended December 31, 2001

Net sales	$900,000
Expenses	
Cost of goods sold	550,000
Selling and administrative expense	133,000
Total expenses	683,000
Income before income taxes	217,000
Income taxes	65,400
Net income	$151,600

Other data:

a.   Cost of goods sold includes depreciation expense of $20,000.
b.   Selling   and   administrative   expense   includes   goodwill
     amortization of $10,000.
c.   Decrease in deferred income taxes (a liability account),
     $5,000.
d.   Increase in accounts receivable, $20,000.
e.   Increase in accounts payable, $10,000.
f.   Increase in inventories, $30,000.
g.   Decrease in income taxes payable, $20,000.

Required:
a.   Prepare a cash basis income statement.
b.   Prepare the cash flows from operating activities, using the
     indirect approach.

SOLUTION:

a.

Pat Gibson Company
Income Statement (Cash Basis)
For the Year Ended December 31, 2001

Collections from customers:
  Sales $900,000
  Increase in receivables   < 20,000> $880,000

Cash paid for merchandise:
  Cost of goods sold $550,000
  Increase in inventory   30,000
  Increase in accounts payable   < 10,000>
  Depreciation expense   < 20,000> <550,000>

Cash payments for selling and
  administrative:
  Selling and administrative expense $133,000
  Goodwill amortization   < 10,000> <123,000>

Cash payments for income taxes:
  Income taxes $ 65,400
  Decrease in deferred income taxes   5,000
  Decrease in income taxes payable   20,000 < 90,400>

Net cash inflow $116,600

b. Cash Flows from Operating Activities

Net income $151,600
Adjustments to reconcile net income to cash
 provided by operating activities:
  Depreciation $ 20,000
  Goodwill amortization   10,000
  Decrease in deferred income taxes   < 5,000>
  Increase in accounts receivable   < 20,000>
  Increase in accounts payable   10,000
  Increase in inventories   < 30,000>
  Decrease in income taxes payable   < 20,000>
Net cash provided by operating activities $116,600

9.

Required:
For each of the following situations, give a likely reason or explanation:

a.   For Jones Company, net cash provided by operating activities is significantly less than net income.
b.   Significant cash outflows were used for investing activities.

c.   The ratio operating cash flow/total debt decreases, while the ratio operating cash flow/current maturities of long-term debt and current notes payable increases.

SOLUTION:

a.   This could be caused by significant increases in current assets that relate to operations or decreases in current liabilities that relate to operations. The most likely reason is a significant increase in accounts receivable and/or inventory.

b.   Significant funds were likely used for investments and/or property, plant, and equipment.

c.   Total debt decreased in relation to cash flow, while current maturities of long-term debt and current notes payable increased in relation to cash flow. This indicates that the company's ability to pay current debt has decreased, while the company's ability to pay total debt has increased.

Chapter 11: EXPANDED ANALYSIS

MULTIPLE CHOICE

e 1. Which of the following ratios is given the highest
       significance rating by commercial loan officers?
       a. Inventory Turnover In Days
       b. Degree of Financial Leverage
       c. Times Interest Earned
       d. Fixed Charge Coverage
       e. Debt/Equity

c 2. Which financial ratio appears most frequently in loan
       agreements according to commercial loan officers?
       a. Quick Ratio
       b. Cash Flow/Total Debt
       c. Debt/Equity
       d. Times Interest Earned
       e. Cash ratio

b 3. Which of the following ratios is given the highest
       significance rating by controllers?
       a. Current Ratio
       b. Earning Per Share
       c. Return on Equity - After Tax
       d. Return on Assets - After Tax
       e. Price/Earnings Ratio

a 4. Which of the following ratios appears most frequently in
       annual reports?
       a. Earnings Per Share
       b. Return on Equity
       c. Profit Margin
       d. Effective Tax Rate
       e. Debt/Equity

d 5. Which of the following ratios is given the highest
       significance rating by Certified Public Accountants?
       a. Quick Ratio
       b. Debt/Equity
       c. Net Profit Margin
       d. Current Ratio
       e. Times Interest Earned

b 6. Which of the following ratios is rated to be a primary
       measure of liquidity and the highest significance rating
       of the liquidity ratios according to commercial loan
       departments?
       a. Debt/Equity
       b. Current Ratio
       c. Degree of Financial Leverage
       d. Inventory Turnover in Days
       e. Accounts Receivable Turnover in Days

d   7.   Which of the following ratios is a primary measure of
             liquidity according to the corporate controller survey?
             a.   earnings per share
             b.   debt/equity ratio
             c.   return on equity after tax
             d.   accounts receivable turnover in days
             e.   none of the above

c   8.   Which of the following depreciation methods is
             considered to be the least conservative?
             a.   sum-of-the-years' digits
             b.   declining-balance method
             c.   straight-line
             d.   each method is equally conservative
             e.   (a) and (b) are equally conservative

a   9.   There are many definitions or descriptions given to
             financial failure. Which of the following does **not**
             appear to be a reasonable definition or description.
             a.   refinancing of bonds payable
             b.   liquidation
             c.   deferment of payments to short-term creditors
             d.   deferment of payments of interest on bonds
             e.   deferment of payments of principal on bonds.

e   10.   Edward I. Altman developed a multivariate model to
             predict bankruptcy. The model produces an overall
             discriminant score called a Z value. Which of the
             following statements is probably an _unreasonable_
             statement relating to the Z value?
             a.   The sales generating ability of the firm's assets is
                  one of the important considerations in the Z value.
             b.   The lack of a market value for a company's stock
                  will reduce the significance of the Z value
                  approach.
             c.   Total assets is an important consideration in the Z
                  value computation.
             d.   Cumulative profitability over time is considered in
                  the Z value computation.
             e.   A Z score of 2.00 or below indicates a very healthy
                  company.

c   11. Which of the following statements is **not** true?
        a. The depreciation method and the period of time
            selected to depreciate an asset can have a
            significant influence on income.
        b. There are many depreciation methods.
        c. The depreciation methods that recognize a large
            amount of depreciation in the later years of an
            asset's life are conservative.
        d. The straight-line depreciation method recognizes
            depreciation in equal amounts over each year of the
            life of the asset.
        e. There is sometimes a material difference in the
            lives used for depreciation between firms.

e   12. In financial accounting, which of the following assets
        is **not** considered to be an intangible asset?
        a. goodwill
        b. patents
        c. copyrights
        d. trademarks
        e. accounts receivable

e   13. Which of the following statements is **not** true?
        a. A review of financial statements, including the
            footnotes, will indicate how conservative the
            statements are in regard to accounting policies.
        b. Accounting policies that result in the slowest
            reporting of income are the most conservative.
        c. When a firm has conservative accounting policies, it
            is said that its earnings are of high quality.
        d. Under inflationary conditions, the least
            conservative inventory method is fifo.
        e. Conservative accounting policies always result in
            the lowest reported income for any given period of
            time.

TRUE/FALSE

T   1. Most of the ratios given a high significance rating by
        commercial loan officers have a primary measure of
        liquidity or debt.

F   2. Ratios with a primary measure of profitability appear
        frequently in loan agreements.

T   3. In general, controllers rate profitability ratios to
        have a higher significance than debt ratios.

T   4. It is logical that there would be a high correlation
        between ratios that are rated to be highly significant
        and ratios that are included in corporate objectives.

T   5.   A review of the computational methodology used to compute the ratios for annual reports indicated that there were wide differences of opinion on how many of the ratios should have been computed.

F   6.   There is a major effort to explain financial results by the disclosure of financial ratios in annual reports.

T   7.   Presently, no regulatory agency, such as the Securities and Exchange Commission or the Financial Accounting Standards Board, accepts responsibility for determining either the content of financial ratios or the format of presentation in annual reports.

T   8.   There are many practical and theoretical issues related to the computation of financial ratios.

F   9.   Accounting policies that result in the fastest reporting of income are the most conservative.

F   10.   Under inflationary conditions, the least conservative inventory method is lifo.

T   11.   The completed-contract method recognizes all income when the contract is completed, while the percentage-of-completion method recognizes income as work progresses on the contract. The completed-contract method is the conservative method.

F   12.   The straight-line depreciation method recognizes depreciation in equal amounts over each year of the life of the asset. Therefore, the straight-line depreciation method is a conservative depreciation method.

T   13.   Most of the ratios given a high significance rating by Chartered Financial Analysts have a primary measure of profitability.

T   14.   Substantial research and development will result in more conservative earnings.

F   15.   The conservative firm will expense goodwill over a relatively long period of time.

F   16.   The interest rate that is assumed to be earned on pension funds can have a material influence on the pension expense and the pension liability. The higher the rate of interest assumed to be earned on pension funds, the higher the pension expense and the higher the pension liability.

T   17.   A univariate model to predict financial failure uses a single variable in a prediction model.

F 18. Beaver did a study that indicated that failed firms have less cash but more inventory one year before failure than do similar firms that do not fail.

T 19. It is likely that particular attention should be paid to cash, accounts receivable, and inventory when forecasting financial failure.

F 20. With the Altman model, the higher the Z score the more likely the firm will go bankrupt.

T 21. An auditor can use financial ratios in analytical review procedures.

T 22. Ideally, a proposed comprehensive budget should be compared with financial ratios that have been agreed upon as part of the firm's corporate objectives.

T 23. The information on a firm's lifo reserve can be used to improve the analysis of inventory, liquidity in general, and the debt position.

T 24. Profitability ratios are the most likely ratios to be selected for corporate objectives.

F 25. A column graph has columns in horizontal form.

T 26. Visually, a pie graph can mislead because of an illusion.

T 27. Analytical review procedures may be performed at various times within the audit.

F 28. A decline in the acid-test ratio indicates a reduced ability to pay current liabilities with funds from the sale of inventory.

PROBLEMS

1.

Firm Using Lifo Inventory	2001	2000
Selected Balance Sheet Data:		
Merchandise inventories	$ 24,000	$ 22,000
Total current assets	41,000	39,000
Total assets	85,000	75,000
Total current liabilities	25,000	24,000
Total long-term debt	30,000	30,000
Selected Income Statement Data:		
Net sales	$360,000	$320,000
Cost of merchandise sold	295,000	260,000
Net income	4,200	4,500
Net income per common share	$2.60	$2.80
Effective tax rate	40%	40%

Selected partial footnote with 2001 financial statements:
Inventories have been reduced by $10,000 and $7,000 at
December 31, 2001, and December 31, 2000 respectively, from
amounts which would have been reported under the fifo method
(which approximated current cost). Had the company valued
all of its inventories under the fifo method, net income
would have been approximately $5,600 in 2001 and $5,601 in
2000.

Required:
a.   Compute the following ratios for 2001 from the financial
     statements (using lifo):
     1.   Days' Sales in Inventory
     2.   Working Capital
     3.   Current Ratio
     4.   Debt Ratio
b.   Compute the following ratios for 2001, using fifo
     disclosure:
     1.   Days' Sales in Inventory
     2.   Working Capital
     3.   Current Ratio
     4.   Debt Ratio
c.   Comment on the difference in the indicated liquidity and
     debt between the ratios computed under lifo and the ratios
     computed under fifo.

SOLUTION:

a.   1.   Days' Sales in Inventory $= \dfrac{\text{Ending Inventory}}{\text{Cost of Goods Sold}/365}$

          $\dfrac{\$24,000}{\$295,000/365} = 29.69$ Days

     2.   Working Capital = Current Assets - Current Liabilities

          $41,000 - \$25,000 = \$16,000$

     3.   Current Ratio $= \dfrac{\text{Current Assets}}{\text{Total Assets}}$

          $\dfrac{\$41,000}{\$25,000} = 1.64$

     4.   Debt Ratio $= \dfrac{\text{Total Liabilities}}{\text{Total Assets}}$

          $\dfrac{\$25,000 + \$30,000}{\$85,000} = 64.71\%$

b.   1.   Days' Sales in Inventory $= \dfrac{\text{Ending Inventory}}{\text{Cost of Goods Sold}/365}$

$$\frac{\$24,000 + \$10,000}{\$295,000 - \$3,000)/365} = 42.50$$

2. Working Capital = Current Assets - Current Liabilities

   ($41,000 + $10,000) - ($25,000 + $4,000) = $22,000

   Increase in tax liability:
   40% x 10,000 = $4,000

3. Current Ratio = $\dfrac{\text{Current Assets}}{\text{Current Liabilities}}$

   $\dfrac{\$51,000}{\$29,000}$ = 1.76

4. Debt Ratio = $\dfrac{\text{Total Liabilities}}{\text{Total Assets}}$

   $\dfrac{\$25,000 + \$30,000 + \$4,000}{\$85,000 + \$10,000}$ = 62.11%

c. Days' Sales in Inventory - The adjusted days' sales in inventory using the fifo data indicates that there is substantially more days' sales in inventory than that indicated using lifo.
   The adjusted ratio is a better indicator because the inventory figure is closer to current cost than under lifo.

   Working Capital - The adjusted working capital is substantially higher than the working capital under lifo.
   The adjusted working capital is a better indicator because of the more realistic inventory amount.

   Current Ratio - The adjusted current ratio is higher than the current ratio computed using the lifo figures.
   The adjusted current ratio is a better indicator because of the more realistic inventory.

   Debt Ratio - The adjusted debt ratio indicates a slightly better debt position than does the unadjusted ratio.
   The adjusted ratio is a better indication of the debt position because of the more realistic inventory and liabilities.

2.

The following data are presented for Zero Company.

Working capital	$60,000
Total assets	400,000
Retained earnings	20,000
Earnings before interest and taxes	40,000
Market value of equity	80,000
Book value of total debt	200,000
Sales	300,000

Z score formula:

$Z = .012X_1 + .014X_2 + .033X_3 + .006X_4 + .010X_5$

X1 = Working Capital/Total Assets
X2 = Retained Earnings (balance sheet)/Total Assets
X3 = Earnings Before Interest and Taxes/Total Assets
X4 = Market Value of Equity/Book Value of Total Debt
X5 = Sales/Total Assets

Required:
a.   Compute the Z score for Zero Company.
b.   Considering the Altman model, comment on the likelihood that this firm will experience financial failure.

SOLUTION:

a. $Z = .012 (\$60,000/\$400,000) + .014 (\$20,000/\$400,000)$
        $+ .033 (\$40,000/\$400,000) + .006 (\$80,000/\$200,000)$
        $+ .010 (\$300,000/\$400,000)$

Z =	.012 (15.00)	= .18	Z = 1.57
	+ .014 (5.00)	.07	
	+ .033 (10.00)	.33	
	+ .006 (40.00)	.24	
	+ .010 (75.00)	.75	

b.   The Z score is 1.57. For a study that covered the period 1970-1973, a Z score of 2.675 was established as a practical cutoff point. Firms that scored below 2.675 are assumed to have similar characteristics of past failures.

3.

The following data are presented for Rocket Company.

Working capital	$100,000
Total assets	300,000
Retained earnings	40,000
Earnings before interest and taxes	60,000
Market value of equity	100,000
Book value of total debt	220,000
Sales	400,000

Z Score Formula:
Z = .012x1 + .014x2 + .033x3 + .006x4 + .010x5
x1 = Working Capital/Total Assets
x2 = Retained Earnings (balance sheet)/Total Assets
x3 = Earnings Before Interest and Taxes/Total Assets
x4 = Market Value of Equity/Book Value of Total Debt
x5 = Sales/Total Assets

Required:
a.   Compute the Z score for Rocket Company.
b.   Considering the Altman model, comment on the likelihood
     that this firm will experience financial failure.

SOLUTION:

a.   Z = .012 ($100,000/$300,000) + .014 ($40,000/$300,000)
         + .033 ($60,000/$300,000) + .006 ($100,000/$220,000)
         + .010 ($400,000/$300,000)

     Z = .012 (33.33)   =   .40
         .014 (13.33)   =   .19
         .033 (20.00)   =   .66
         .006 (45.45)   =   .27
         .010 (133.33)   = 1.33
                     Z   = 2.85

b.   The Z score is 2.85. For a study that covered the period
     1970-1973, a Z score of 2.675 was established as a
     practical cutoff point. Firms that score below 2.675 are
     assumed to have similar characteristics of past failures.

Chapter 12: SPECIAL INDUSTRIES:BANKS, UTILITIES, OIL AND GAS, TRANSPORTATION,INSURANCE, REAL ESTATE COMPANIES

MULTIPLE CHOICE

d   1.   A characteristic common to banks, utilities, and
          transportation is that they:
               a. are all government owned
          b.   are not subject to the rules of the FASB
          c.   are monopolies
          d.   each have a uniform system of accounts established
               by a federal regulatory agency
          e.   never go bankrupt

c   2.   Which of the following is **not** an asset of a bank?
          a.   bank building
          b.   accrued interest receivable
          c.   savings deposits
          d.   loans
          e.   investment securities

e   3.   Which of the following is most likely the largest
          expense of a bank?
          a.   income taxes
          b.   occupancy expense
          c.   salaries
          d.   interest on loans
          e.   interest on deposits

c   4.   Total deposits times capital is:
          a.   a type of interest coverage ratio
          b.   a profit measure
          c.   a type of debt to equity ratio
          d.   similar to net working capital
          e.   a type of asset to liability ratio

e   5.   Which of the following organizations does **not** require
          that banks report to it?
          a.   Internal Revenue Service
          b.   Federal Reserve System
          c.   Comptroller of the Currency
          d.   Federal Deposit Insurance Corporation
          e.   Interstate Commerce Commission

c   6.   What is the best description of the nature of checking
          accounts of customers on the balance sheet of a bank?
          a.   short-term asset
          b.   long-term asset
          c.   short-term liability
          d.   long-term liability
          e.   owners' equity

d 7. The principal revenue source for a bank typically is:
a. gain on sale of real estate
b. sales
c. dividend income
d. interest income
e. interest expense

a 8. Which of the following is **not** a type of earning asset for a bank?
a. cash
b. loans
c. leases
d. investment securities
e. money market assets

b 9. Interest margin to average total assets measures:
a. the balance between earning and non-earning assets
b. management's ability to control the spread between interest income and interest expense
c. the ability to borrow successfully
d. the proportion of debt to equity
e. the return on owner's investment

d 10. One reason for the relatively stable earnings of utilities is:
a. the use of high leverage
b. local service
c. uniform accounting
d. utilities are regulated because of non-duplication of service
e. none of the above

d 11. The first balance sheet asset for a utility is:
a. cash
b. receivables
c. inventory
d. plant
e. investments

c 12. Inventory is a relatively small asset for electric utilities because:
a. they are valued at cost rather than market
b. they are valued at lower of cost or market
c. the product is not stored
d. the inventory turnover in days is relatively high
e. none of the above

e   13.   Accounting for Utilities, banks, and transportation
           firms is similar in that:
           a.   all are monopolies
           b.   all report property, plant, and equipment first on
                the balance sheet
           c.   all are controlled by the Interstate Commerce
                Commission
           d.   all carry heavy inventory
           e.   all utilize some form of uniform accounting system

a   14.   The presentation of revenue may differ in a
           transportation firm by having:
           a.   revenue classified by user group
           b.   expenses precede revenue
           c.   revenue presented on a per share basis
           d.   revenue classified as a balance sheet liability
           e.   revenue categorized by geographic origin

d   15.   In analyzing the borrowing position of a utility, which
           of the following is primary?
           a.   liquidity
           b.   ability to earn a profit
           c.   return to shareholders
           d.   long-term debt capacity
           e.   utilization of current assets

c   16.   Funded debt to operating property is a measure of:
           a.   profitability
           b.   return to shareholders
           c.   debt coverage
           d.   liquidity
           e.   asset turnover

d   17.   Which of the following will **not** cause the percent earned
           on operating property of a utility to fall?
           a.   sale of a fully depreciated asset at a loss
           b.   building a new plant
           c.   increase in operating expenses
           d.   decrease in borrowing and interest expense
           e.   decrease in revenue

a   18.   Which of the following have a balance sheet similar in
           format to a manufacturing firm?
           a.   transportation
           b.   banks
           c.   utilities
           d.   a and c
           e.   a and b

c   19. The operating ratio of Cross America Airlines has
          increased. Which of the following could **not** explain
          this rise?
          a. Operating revenues have increased more slowly than
              expenses.
          b. Salary costs have risen substantially.
          c. Operating revenues have increased with stable
              operating expenses.
          d. Dues costs have risen substantially.
          e. None of the above.

d   20. The largest asset for airlines will usually be:
          a. accounts receivable
          b. inventory of spare parts
          c. investment in subsidiaries
          d. flight equipment
          e. ground equipment

a   21. The operating ratio for a railroad is a measure of:
          a. cost control
          b. liquidity
          c. earnings to investors
          d. borrowing ability
          e. liquidity

b   22. Data per passenger-mile is often used by transportation
          companies to analyze:
          a. current ratio
          b. revenue
          c. borrowing ability
          d. earnings per share
          e. leverage

d   23. Under the full-cost approach to oil and gas accounting:
          a. costs related to successful efforts are expensed and
              others capitalized
          b. cost related to successful efforts are capitalized
              and others expensed
          c. all costs are expensed as incurred
          d. all costs are capitalized as incurred
          e. only the cost of buildings and equipment are
              capitalized

e   24. Which of the following will cause operating revenues for
          a transportation firm to vary?
          a. difference in rates
          b. classification of traffic
          c. volume of traffic carried
          d. distance traffic is transported
          e. all of the above

a   25. There are basically four types of insurance
          organizations. Which of the following is **not** one of
          these four types?
          a. group
          b. stock companies
          c. mutual companies
          d. fraternal benefit societies
          e. assessment companies

e   26. Insurance companies tend to have a stock market price at
          a discount to the average market price (price/earnings
          ratio). Which of the following is **not** a likely reason
          for this relatively low market value?
          a. Insurance is a highly regulated industry.
          b. The insurance industry has substantial competition.
          c. The accounting environment likely contributes to the
              relatively low market price for insurance company
              stocks.
          d. The nature of the industry leads to standards that
              provide for much judgment and possible manipulation
              of reported profit.
          e. Insurance companies typically have a high return on
              common equity.

TRUE/FALSE

T   1.   Banks operate either under a federal or state charter.

F   2.   Banks are always restricted from operating interstate.

F   3.   All banks belong to a bank holding company.

T   4.   For a bank holding company, in order for ratio analysis
          to be meaningful, a large portion of the services should
          be bank-related.

F   5.   The provision for loan losses for a bank is the same as
          the allowance for doubtful accounts.

F   6.   The report of income and dividends is the same as a
          balance sheet for a bank.

F   7.   The principal asset of a bank is property and equipment.

T   8.   For a bank, loans to customers are assets.

F   9.   For a bank, loans are not earning assets.

F   10. Interest margin is the spread between interest income
          and net income for a bank.

T   11. The loan loss coverage ratio for a bank determines the
          asset quality.

F   12.   The loan loss coverage ratio is computed by dividing the provision for loans by net loans.

T   13.   Equity capital to total assets for a bank is a measure of leverage.

T   14.   Loans to deposits for a bank is a type of debt coverage ratio.

T   15.   A distinguishing factor about utilities is that generally their services are not duplicated by another firm.

F   16.   Uniformity of accounting for interstate electric companies is prescribed by the Interstate Commerce Commission.

T   17.   For a utility, the first item listed under liabilities and equity is capital stock.

F   18.   Most utilities have very high receivables.

F   19.   A profitable utility will maintain a high operating ratio.

T   20.   In the ratio funded debt to operating property for a utility, construction in progress is a component of operating property.

F   21.   In the case of air carriers, the cost of goods sold section of the income statement looks similar to that of a steel manufacturer.

F   22.   Inventory turnover is a valuable tool for analyzing a railroad.

T   23.   Operating revenue to operating property for a railroad is a turnover type ratio.

T   24.   A good statistic for analysis of asset utilization for a bus line is the passenger load factor.

T   25.   The passenger load factor measures the percent that a carrier is filled, based on capacity.

T   26.   Monitoring cash flow can be particularly important when following an oil or gas company.

F   27.   Large oil and gas companies tend to select a variation of the full-cost method to account for exploration and production costs.

T 28. The successful efforts method places only exploration
        and production costs of successful wells on the balance
        sheet under property, plant, and equipment.

T 29. A basic issue, still unresolved, relates to whether oil
        and gas exploration cost should be expensed or
        capitalized.

F 30. The financial statement format for regulated firms will
        never differ from those of manufacturers and retailers;
        the format is prescribed by the FASB.

T 31. A review of the assets of a bank may indicate that the
        bank has a substantial investment in long-term bonds.
        Such an investment could reflect substantial risk if
        interest rates increase.

F 32. The value of fixed rate mortgages could decline
        substantially if interest rates decreased.

T 33. Real estate companies contend that conventional
        accounting, recognizing depreciation but not the
        underlying value of the property, misleads investors.

T 34. A review of the disclosure of allowance for loan losses
        for a bank may indicate significant losses charged.

F 35. Electric utilities that have substantial construction
        work in progress are usually viewed as being less risky
        investments than electric utilities that do not have
        substantial construction work in progress.

F 36. For an electric utility, the account allowance for
        equity funds used during construction represents the
        cost of borrowed funds that are used for construction.

T 37. The utility is building into the cost base an amount for
        an assumed rate of return on equity funds by increasing
        the balance sheet account, construction work in
        progress, for an assumed rate of return on equity funds.

T 38. It is generally perceived that utilities that have cash
        flow problems will not be increasing their dividend.

T 39. Insurance companies provide two types of services. One
        service is an identified contract service - mortality
        protection or loss protection. The second service
        consists of investment management service.

F 40. Regulation of insurance companies started at the federal
        level.

T   41.   Statutory accounting has emphasized the balance sheet in
          its concern for protecting the policyholders by focusing
          on the financial solvency of the insurance corporation.

F   42.   Generally accepted accounting principles for insurance
          companies developed much sooner than statutory
          accounting practices.

T   43.   The balance sheets of insurance companies are not
          classified by current assets and current liabilities.

F   44.   If an insurance company does not intend to hold bonds
          until maturity, the bonds are reported at cost.

T   45.   Insurance companies carry real estate investments at
          cost less accumulated depreciation and an allowance for
          impairment in value.

T   46.   Deferred policy acquisition costs represent the cost of
          obtaining policies. Under statutory accounting
          practices, these costs are charged to expense.

T   47.   Insurance companies have been accused of over-reserving
          during tough years.

T   48.   The stockholders' equity section of an insurance company
          will usually appear similar to the stockholders' equity
          section of other industries.

T   49.   The manner of recognizing revenue on insurance contracts
          is unique for the insurance industry. In general the
          duration of the contract governs the revenue
          recognition.

F   50.   For insurance companies, realized gains and losses from
          investments are not reported in operations in the period
          incurred.

PROBLEMS

1.

The controller of Central Bank has computed certain ratios for
the bank and a competitor, Southern County Bank. These
activities are presented below:

	Ratios	Year	Central Bank	Southern County Bank
a.	Total deposits times capital	2000	12.1 times	11.6 times
		1999	12.2 times	11.5 times

b.   Loans to
        total deposits   2000   71.4%   67.2%
                                1999   70.1%   67.0%

c.   Capital funds
        to total assets   2000   7.3%   8.1%
                                1999   7.4%   8.0%

Required:
Briefly explain the meaning of each ratio and then compare the firms for each ratio. How do the firms compare overall?

SOLUTION:

a.   Total deposits times capital is a type of debt to equity ratio. More capital implies a greater margin of safety.

      Central Bank has a higher ratio of total deposits times capital, giving slightly greater risk for Central Bank.

b.   Loans to total deposits is a type of asset to liability ratio. More loans imply assets to cover the deposits, which may be withdrawn on request.

      Central Bank has higher loans to total deposits. This gives greater coverage of the deposit liability, although it can also imply more risky loans.

c.   Capital funds to total assets is a measure of equity ownership in the bank. It provides the cushion against the use of debt.

      Central Bank has a lower capital funds to total assets ratio, indicating less equity ownership and more debt.

d.   Overall, Central Bank is in a riskier position.

2.

The following statistics are presented for 2001 and 2000 for National Community Bank:

(in thousands)	2001	2000
Average loans	$ 436,000	$ 448,000
Average total assets	1,250,000	1,225,000
Average earning assets	900,000	880,000
Average total deposits	850,000	894,000
Average total equity	75,000	68,000
Interest expense	99,000	79,000
Interest income	149,000	119,000

Required:
For each year:
a.   1. Calculate the deposits times capital.

2. Calculate the loans to deposits.
3. Calculate the equity capital to total assets.
4. Calculate the interest margin to average total assets.

b. Comment on the results in 1-4, using the perspective of a shareholder.

SOLUTION:

			2001	2000
a.	1.	Deposits Times Capital	$ 850,000 75,000	$ 894,000 68,000
			11.33 times	13.15 times
	2.	Loans Deposits	$436,000 $850,000	$448,000 $894,000
			51.29%	50.11%
	3.	Equity Total Assets	$ 75,000 $1,250,000	$68,000 $1,225,000
			6.00%	5.56%
	4.	Interest Margin Average Earning Assets	$149,000-$99,000 $900,000	$ 119,000 -$79,000 $ 880,000
			5.56%	4.55%

b. Deposits to capital, a type of debt/equity ratio, has fallen providing a safer position for shareholders. Loans to deposits, a ratio relating assets to liabilities, has improved. Equity to assets shows that shareholders are contributing more funds. Interest margin to average earning assets show improved profitability. Overall, the position of a shareholder shows evidence of higher earnings and less risk.

3.

Required:
a. What is a bank Report of Condition?
b. A local bank has a high loan to total deposits ratio. The controller of the bank feels that there is a problem with the loans, despite the fact that the loan to total deposits ratio is considered a type of debt coverage ratio. Discuss the controller's position.

SOLUTION:
a. A bank Report of Condition is similar to a balance sheet reporting assets and liabilities.

b. A high amount of loans might indicate a number of risky
    borrowers and potential bad debts. This is probably the
    concern of the controller.

4.

Statistics of Lone Star Bank are presented below:

	2001	2000
Provision for loan losses	$ 12,000,000	$ 10,000,000
Net charge-offs	8,700,000	9,800,000
Income before tax and security transactions	41,250,000	47,340,000
Taxes or income before security transactions	11,900,000	16,970,000
Net income before security transactions	29,350,000	30,370,000
Average earning assets	6,200,000,000	6,370,000,000
Average total assets	6,895,000,000	7,000,000,000
Interest margin	240,000,000	225,000,000

Required:
For each year, compute:
a. 1. Earning assets to total assets.
    2. Loan loss coverage ratio.
    3. Interest margin to average earning assets.
b. Comment on the results of 1-3.

SOLUTION:

			2001	2000
a.	1.	Earning Assets	$6,200,000,000	$6,370,000,000
		Total Assets	$6,895,000,000	$7,000,000,000
			89.92%	91.00%

2. Loan Loss Coverage Ratio:

	2001		2000	
Pre-Tax Income +	$	41,250,000	$	47,340,000
Provision for Loan Losses	+	12,000,000	+	10,000,000
Net Charge-Offs	$	8,700,000	$	9,800,000
		6.12 Times		5.85 Times

		2001	2000
3.	Interest Margin	$ 240,000,000	$ 225,000,000
	Average Earning Assets	$6,200,000,000	$6,370,000,000
		3.87%	3.53%

b. The percent of earning assets to total assets has declined
    slightly. The loan loss coverage ratio shows improvement,
    due in part to lower net charge-offs. The interest margin
    to average earning assets has also improved slightly.

5.

Statistics from New State Electric Company annual report are presented below:

	(in millions)	
	2001	2000
Operating revenues	$180	$164
Operating expenses (including federal income taxes)	139	125
Federal income taxes	12	10
Interest deductions	31	27
Earnings available for common stock	8	9
Net plant (operating property)	690	604
Current assets	66	53
Total assets	770	665
Shareholders' equity	262	251
Long-term debt	308	286
Current liabilities	181	119
Total liabilities and shareholders' equity	770	665

Required:
a. Compute the following ratios for 2001 and 2000:
 1. Funded Debt to Operating Property
 2. Times Interest Earned
 3. Operating Revenue to Operating Property
 4. Operating Ratio
b. Comment on the above ratios for the two years.

SOLUTION:

		(in millions)	
		2001	2000
a.	1. Funded Debt (long-term)	$308	$286
	Operating Property	690	604
	Funded Debt to Operating Property	44.6%	47.4%
	2. Operating revenues	$180	$164
	Operating expenses (including federal income taxes)	139	125
	Federal income taxes	12	10
	Operating expenses before taxes	127	115
	Operating income	53	49
	Interest deduction	$ 31	$ 27
	Times interest earned	1.71 Times	1.81 Times
	3. Operating Revenue	$180	$164
	Operating Property	690	604
	Operating Revenue to Operating Property	26.1%	27.2%
	4. Operating Expenses	$139	$125
	Operating Revenues	180	164
	Operating Ratio	77.2%	76.2%

b.   Funded Debt to Operating Property has declined, indicating
      an improved debt position. But the interest coverage has
      declined, indicating a lesser ability to cover the debt.
      The firm is generating slightly less revenue on its
      operating property. The operating expenses have risen in
      relation to revenues. Overall, these ratios show a slight
      erosion of the financial position.

6.

Parts of the operating statistics for Big State Power are given
below:

	(in millions)	
	2001	2000
Operating revenue	$125,000	$98,900
Operating expense	117,000	88,900
Operating property	73,500	57,000
Net income	2,250	3,400
Funded debt	66,000	49,000

Required:
a. Compute the following ratios:
    1. Operating ratio
    2. Funded debt to operating property
    3. Percent earned on operating property
    4. Operating revenue to operating property
b. Discuss the trend in these results.

SOLUTION:

a.

			(in millions)	
			2001	2000
1.	Operating Ratio =	Operating Expenses / Operating Revenue	$117,000 / $125,000	$88,900 / $98,900
			93.6%	89.89%
2.		Funded Debt / Operating Property	$66,000 / $73,500	$49,000 / $57,000
			89.80%	85.96%
3.	Percent Earned on Operating Property	Net Income / Operating Property	$2,250 / $73,500	$3,400 / $57,000
			3.06%	5.96%
4.		Operating Revenue / Operating Property	$125,000 / $73,500	$98,900 / $57,000
			1.70 times	1.74 times

b.   This firm shows a decline in profitability, both from the
       high operating ratio and the drop in the earnings on
       operating property. Part of the cause may be the rise in
       the percentage of funded debt. Also, the turnover of
       operating property to generate sales has fallen.

7.

Purple Tortoise Bus Company had the following operating results
in the past two years:

	2001	2000
Operating revenues	$ 457,000	$ 310,000
Operating expenses	437,000	285,000
Operating property	212,000	180,000
Net income	6,000	12,000
Long-term debt	170,000	140,000
Estimated passenger miles	4,500,000	3,500,000
Load factor	63%	71%

Required:
a. For each year:
    1.   Calculate the operating ratio and comment on the trend.
    2.   Calculate the long-term debt to operating property
         ratio. What does this tell about debt use?
    3.   Calculate the operating revenue to operating property
         ratio. Comment on the trend.
    4.   Calculate the revenue and income passenger mile and
         discuss.
b.   What does the load factor indicate?

SOLUTION:

a.
                                              2001   2000
  1.   Operating Expenses $437,000 $285,000
       Operating Revenue $457,000 $310,000

                                            95.62%   91.94%

The operating ratio has risen to show a decline in
profitability.

2.   Long-Term Debt $170,000 $140,000
       Operating Property $212,000 $180,000

                                            80.19%   77.78%

The percentage of debt has increased.

3.   Operating Revenue $457,000 $310,000
       Operating Property $212,000 $180,000

                                          2.16 times   1.72 times

Revenue to property shows a higher turnover; hence, this company's problem is not in generating sales, but rather in cost control.

4.

Revenue	$ 457,000	$ 310,000
Passenger Miles	4,500,000	3,500,000
	10.16¢	8.86¢

Revenue per passenger-mile has risen showing price increases.

Net Income	$ 6,000	$ 12,000
Passenger Miles	4,500,000	3,500,000
	.0013¢	.0034¢

Profits have declined in relation to passenger miles, while revenue has increased.

b.   The load factor indicates that the buses were less full in 2001 than in 2000.

8.

Required:
a.   Worldwide Airlines has had an increase in revenue per passenger mile, but a decline in earnings per share. Explain this apparent contradiction in profit measures.

b.   It is sometimes said that the use of leverage is more favorable for utilities than for transportation firms.   Why is this statement true?

SOLUTION:

a.   An increase in revenue per passenger mile simply means an increase in fares for routes.   However, lower use by passengers can mean lower revenue.   Further, per mile measures do not evaluate expenses, which may be fixed and high for airlines.

b.   Leverage works better when earnings are relatively stable or steadily rising.   With fluctuating earnings, the financial leverage causes magnification of both the increases and decreases.

Utilities usually have more stable earnings than do transportation firms.   Therefore, leverage usually works more to the advantage of the shareholder in a utility than for the shareholder in a transportation firm.

9.

Searing, Inc. made several drills for oil in 2001. The following
data represent its results:

Total costs	$18,000,000
Total wells drilled	10
Good wells	6
Dry wells	4

Assume that each well cost the same amount to drill.

Required:
a. Determine the amount to be capitalized and the amount to be
    expensed if the successful-efforts method is used.
b. Determine the amount to be capitalized and the amount to be
    expensed if the full-cost method is used.

SOLUTION:
a. $\frac{\text{6 Good Wells}}{\text{10 Total Wells Drilled}}$ = 60%

    60% x $18,000,000 = $10,800,000   Capitalize

    40% x $18,000,000 = $ 7,200,000   Expense

b.   Capitalize all $18,000,000.

MULTIPLE CHOICE

e   1.   Which of the following is **not** an example of a nonprofit
          institution?
          a.   university
          b.   hospital
          c.   state government
          d.   church
          e.   none of the above

b   2.   Cash receipts and disbursements related to the payment
          of interest and principal on long-term debt describe
          which of the following?
          a.   appropriations
          b.   debt service
          c.   capital projects
          d.   general fund
          e.   proprietary funds

c   3.   All cash receipts and disbursements not required to be
          accounted for in another fund are accounted for in which
          of the following funds?
          a.   fiduciary fund
          b.   proprietary fund
          c.   general fund
          d.   debt service fund
          e.   special assessment fund

d   4.   Which of the following, in accounting for governments,
          provides necessary resources and the authority for their
          disbursements?
          a.   general fund
          b.   encumbrances
          c.   internal services
          d.   appropriations
          e.   special assessments

d   5.   For a statement of changes in net worth, which of the
          following would be a realized decrease in net worth?
          a.   dividend income
          b.   change in value of land
          c.   decrease in value of boat
          d.   personal expenditures
          e.   salary

a   6. For a statement of changes in net worth, which of the following would be an unrealized decrease in net worth?
   a. decrease in value of furnishings
   b. salary
   c. income taxes
   d. increase in value of land
   e. interest income

e   7. Which of the following would **not** be a source of information for personal financial statements?
   a. broker's statements
   b. income tax returns
   c. safe deposit box
   d. checkbook
   e. all of the above would be a source of information

b   8. Which of the following would **not** likely be a reason for preparing personal financial statements?
   a. obtaining personal credit
   b. determining the tax basis of marketable securities
   c. income tax planning
   d. retirement planning
   e. estate planning

a   9. Which of the following would **not** be a reasonable suggestion for reviewing the Statement of Financial Condition?
   a. Determine unrealized increases in net worth.
   b. Determine the personal net worth amount.
   c. Determine the amounts of the assets that are very liquid.
   d. Determine the due period of liabilities.
   e. Determine specific assets and specific liabilities.

e   10. Which of the following would **not** be an acceptable presentation on a personal financial statement?
   a. Marketable securities are presented at estimated current values.
   b. The estimated current value of an investment in life insurance is the cash value of the policy less the amount of any loans against it.
   c. Investments in real estate should be presented at their estimated current values.
   d. Payables and other liabilities should be presented at the discounted amounts of cash to be paid.
   e. The liability for income taxes payable includes unpaid income taxes for completed tax years only.

TRUE/FALSE

T   1.   Personal financial statements are financial statements of individuals, husband and wife, or a larger family group.

F   2.   Personal financial statements predominately use historical cost information.

F   3.   The basic statement prepared for personal financial statements is the statement of changes in net worth.

T   4.   For personal financial statements, the statement of financial condition is similar to a balance sheet.

T   5.   The statement of changes in net worth is presented in terms of realized increases (decreases) and unrealized increases (decreases).

F   6.   The concept of a personal income statement does not apply to personal financial statements.

F   7.   For a statement of financial condition, usually the figure that will be most important is the total asset amount.

T   8.   The accounting for a nonprofit institution does not include a single entity concept or efficiency.

F   9.   The principal of fiduciary funds may be distributed.

T   10.   The Governmental Accounting Standards Board is a branch of the Financial Accounting Foundation.

T   11.   State and local governments serve as a steward over public funds. This stewardship responsibility dominates the accounting for state and local governments.

F   12.   The budget for a state or local government is merely a plan of future revenues and expenses.

F   13.   The rating for an industrial revenue bond represents the probability of default by the governmental unit.

T   14.   When reviewing the financial reporting of governmental units, it is helpful to visualize the reporting in a pyramid fashion.

T   15.   Nonprofit institutions, other than governments, use forms of financial reporting that vary from the fund type of system to a commercial type of reporting.

T   16.   Some nonprofit institutions have added budgeting by objectives and/or measures of productivity to their financial reporting.

F   17.   Personal financial statements present assets at their historical cost.

T   18.   Personal financial statements should present receivables at the discounted amounts of cash the person estimates will be collected, using appropriate interest rates at the date of the financial statements.

T   19.   Several procedures or combinations of procedures may be used to determine the estimated current value of a closely held business.

F   20.   The statement of changes in net worth is required when presenting personal financial statements.

T   21.   In general SFAS No. 116 directs that contributions received are recognized as revenues in the period received at their fair value.

PROBLEMS

1.

Required: Match the definitions to the terms.

Term	Definition
___ 1. appropriations	a. Cash receipts and disbursements related to the payment of interest and principal on long-term debt.
___ 2. debt Service	b. Cash receipts and disbursements related to improvements or services for which special property assessments have been levied.
___ 3. capital projects	c. Service centers that supply goods or services to other governmental units on a cost reimbursement basis.
___ 4. special assessments	d. Intention is to maintain the fund's assets through cost reimbursement by users or partial cost recovery from users and periodic infusion of additional assets.
___ 5. internal services	e. Future commitments for expenditure.
___ 6. enterprises	f. Provide necessary resources and the authority for their disbursements.

_____ 7. proprietary funds

g. Cash receipts and disbursements related to the acquisition of long-lived assets.

_____ 8. general fund

h. Operations that are similar to private businesses where service users are charged fees.

_____ 9. fiduciary funds

i. All cash receipts and disbursements not required to be accounted for in another fund.

_____ 10. encumbrances

j. The principal of these funds must remain intact. Typically revenues earned may be distributed.

SOLUTION:

1. f	5. c	9. j
2. a	6. h	10. e
3. g	7. d	
4. b	8. i	

2.

Required:

a. Pat and Lou Krammer purchased their home in Mt. Vernon in 1987 for $60,000. The unpaid mortgage is $10,000. A new roof was added for $4,000 immediately after the purchase. Real estate prices in Mt. Vernon increased 20% since the purchase. What amount should be shown on the Krommer statement of financial condition?

b. Dick Roth bought a home in 1986 for $100,000. Currently, the mortgage on the home is $30,000. Because of the current high interest rates, the bank has offered to retire the mortgage for $20,000. What is the estimated current value of this liability?

c. Sue Kern guaranteed a loan of $5,000 for her boyfriend to buy a boat. Sue's boyfriend is behind in payments on the boat. What liability should be shown on Sue's statement of financial condition?

d. Chuck owns 1,000 shares of Tago. Tago is a local company whose stock is sold by a broker on a work-out basis. (The broker tries to find a buyer). The most recent selling price was $5. The commission to sell these securities will be $100. What is the estimated current value of these securities?

e. Anne has a certificate of deposit with a $5,000 balance. Accrued interest is $300. The penalty for early withdrawal is $400. What is the estimated current value of the certificate of deposit?

SOLUTION:

a. $60,000 purchase price
      <u> 4,000</u> improvements
       64,000
      <u>   1.2</u> increase in inflation rate
       76,800
      <u> 10,000</u> less mortgage
      <u>$66,800</u>

b.   If the offer to buy back the mortgage is still outstanding,
      the estimated current value of the debt would be $20,000.
      If the buy back offer has expired, then the estimated
      current value of the mortgage is $30,000.

c.   The guarantee should not be presented as a liability. It
      should be disclosed in a footnote, if material.

d.   1,000 shares x $5 = $5,000
             Less commission   <u>   100</u>
                                  <u>$4,900</u>

e. Certificate of deposit $5,000
         Accrued interest   <u>   300</u>
                                  $5,300

      Less early withdrawal
              penalty   <u>   400</u>
                                 <u>$4,900</u>

3.
For Larry and Carl, the assets and liabilities and the effective
income tax rates are as follows at December 31, 2001:

Account	Tax Bases	Estimated Current Value	Excess of Estimated Current Values Over (Under) Tax Bases	Effective Income Tax Rates	Amount of Estimated Income Taxes
Cash	$10,000	$10,000			
Marketable Securities	20,000	25,000	5,000	16%	
Residence	80,000	100,000	20,000	10%	
Furnishings	20,000	18,000	(2,000)		
Jewelry	5,000	4,000	(1,000)		
Autos	15,000	12,000	(3,000)		
Mortgage Payable	30,000	30,000			
Credit Cards	4,000	4,000			

Required:
a.   Compute the estimated tax liability on the differences
      between the estimated current value of the assets and
      liabilities and their tax bases.
b.   Present a statement of financial condition for Larry and
      Carl at December 31, 2001.

SOLUTION:

a.   Marketable Securities $5,000 x 16% = $ 800
     Residence   20,000 x 10% =   2,000
                                                     $2,800

b.   Larry and Carl
              Statement of Financial Condition
                    December 31, 2001

     Assets
          Cash $ 10,000
          Marketable securities   25,000
          Residence   100,000
          Furnishings   18,000
          Jewelry   4,000
          Autos   12,000
       Total Assets $169,000

     Liabilities:
          Mortgage payable $30,000
          Credit cards   4,000
             Total liabilities   34,000

     Estimated income taxes on
     differences between estimated
     current value of assets and
     their tax basis   2,800

     Net Worth   132,200
       Total liabilities and Net Worth $169,000

4.

For Bob and Jane, the assets and liabilities and the effective
income tax rates are as follows at December 31, 2001:

Account	Tax Bases	Estimate of Current Value	Excess of Estimated Current Values Over Tax Bases	Effective Income Tax Rates	Amount of Estimated Income Taxes
Cash	$30,000	$30,000			
Marketable Securities	50,000	60,000	10,000	20%	
Options	-0-	20,000	20,000	20%	
Residence	120,000	160,000	40,000	10%	
Royalties	-0-	10,000	10,000	20%	
Furnishings	30,000	25,000	(5,000)		
Auto	10,000	8,000	(2,000)		
Mortgage Payable	(60,000)	(60,000)			
Auto Loan	(4,000)	(4,000)			

Required:
a.   Compute the estimated tax liability on the differences
     between the estimated current value of the assets and
     liabilities and their tax bases.

b.   Present a statement of financial condition for Bob and Jane
     at December 31, 2001.

SOLUTION:

a.   Marketable Securities $10,000 x 20% = $2,000
          Options   20,000 x 20% =   4,000
          Residence   40,000 x 10% =   4,000
          Royalties   10,000 x 20% =   2,000
                                                            $12,000

b.   Bob and Jane
                   Statement of Financial Condition
                         December 31, 2001

          Assets
          Cash $ 30,000
          Marketable securities   60,000
          Options   20,000
          Residence   160,000
          Royalties   10,000
          Furnishings   25,000
          Auto   8,000
     Total Assets $313,000

          Liabilities
            Mortgage payable $60,000
            Auto loan   4,000
     Total Liabilities   64,000

          Estimated income taxes on
          differences between estimated
          current value of assets and
          their tax basis   12,000

     Net Worth   237,000
          Total liabilities and Net Worth $313,000

5.

For Bill and Linda, the changes in net worth for the year ended
December 31, 2001, are detailed as follows:

          Realized increases in net worth:
            Salary $ 40,000
            Interest income   5,000

          Realized decreases in net worth:
            Income taxes   10,000
            Interest expenses   8,000
            Personal expenditures   30,000

Unrealized increases in net worth:
  Marketable Securities   3,000
  Land   4,000
  Residence   2,000

Unrealized decreases in net worth:
  Furnishings   2,000
  Estimated income taxes on the
     differences between the
     estimated current amounts
     of liabilities and their
     tax bases   8,000

Net worth at the beginning of year   80,000

Required:
Prepare a statement of changes in net worth for the year ended
December 31, 2001.

SOLUTION:

Bill and Linda
Statement of Changes in Net Worth
For the Year Ended December 31, 2001

Realized increases in net worth:
  Salary $ 40,000
  Interest income   5,000
                                  45,000

Realized decreases in net worth:
  Income taxes   10,000
  Interest expenses   8,000
  Personal expenditures   30,000
                                  48,000

Net realized decreases in
  net worth   (3,000)

Unrealized increases in net worth:
  Marketable Securities   3,000
  Land   4,000
  Residence   2,000
                                  9,000

Unrealized decreases in net worth
  Furnishings   2,000
  Estimated income taxes on the
     differences between the
     estimated current amounts
     of liabilities and their
     tax bases   8,000
                               10,000

Net unrealized decreases in net worth   1,000
Net decrease in net worth   4,000
Net worth at the beginning of the year 80,000
Net worth at the end of the year $ 76,000

13-9

6.

For Howard and Joyce, the changes in net worth for the year ended
December 31, 2001, are detailed as follows:

Realized increases in net worth:	
Salary	$ 50,000
Interest income	500
Dividend income	400
Realized decreases in net worth:	
Income taxes	12,000
Interest expenses	4,000
Personal expenditures	25,000
Unrealized increases in net worth:	
Marketable securities	5,000
Residence	2,000
Unrealized decreases in net worth:	
Furnishings	4,000
Boat	2,000
Estimated income taxes on the differences between the estimated current values of assets and the estimated current amounts of liabilities and their tax bases	7,000
Net worth at the beginning of year	60,000

Required:
Prepare a statement of changes in net worth for the year ended
December 31, 2001.

SOLUTION:

Howard and Joyce
Statement of Changes in Net Worth
For the Year Ended December 31, 2001

Realized increases in net worth:
Salary $ 50,000
Interest income   500
Dividend income   400
                                                     50,900

Realized decreases in net worth:
Income taxes   12,000
Interest expenses   4,000
Personal expenditures   25,000
                                                    41,000
Net realized increases in net worth: 9,900

Unrealized increases in net worth:
Marketable securities   5,000
Residence   2,000
                                                     7,000

Unrealized decreases in net worth:
Furnishings   4,000
Boat   2,000

Estimated income taxes on the
    differences between the
    estimated current amounts
    of liabilities and their
    tax basis   7,000
                                                    13,000
Net unrealized decreases in net worth   (6,000)
Net increase in net worth   3,900
Net worth at the beginning of the year   60,000
Net worth at the end of the year $ 63,900